FREUD AND CONTEMPORARY CULTURE

Etching of Freud from life, by Max Pollak, Vienna, 1921

FREUD AND CONTEMPORARY CULTURE

THE NEW YORK ACADEMY OF MEDICINE

Iago Galdston, M.D., Editor

INTERNATIONAL UNIVERSITIES PRESS, INC.

NEW YORK, 1957

CONTENTS

TABLES

FOREWORD

The New York Academy of Medicine is eight years the senior of the Centenary celebrated in the essays of this volume—that of the birth of Sigmund Freud. In the encompassed hundred years, and more, medicine has experienced greater advancements and a more radical reorientation in its basic conceptions and in its modes of operation than it did in all its antecedent ages.

The New York Academy of Medicine has been not only the witness of, but has in no small measure served, in the personage of its Fellowship, to eventuate these great developments. It is more than fitting then that the Academy should institutionally celebrate the hundredth anniversary of the birth of Sigmund Freud who imprinted the indelible stamp of his genius upon the fabric of contemporary medicine. In taking cognizance of this memorial date we do indeed, and above all else, celebrate his genius which is manifestly great, and leave it to the discrete judgments of time and further experience to assess the validity and merits of his psychological theories and therapeutic techniques. For the two are disparate, as can be seen in the lives of other great scientists, whose works have not withstood the attritional effects of critical judgment, but whose position among the celebrated remains unaffected. It is perhaps this above all else that distinguishes the essays herein presented. They are appreciative but not encomiastical; that is, not without a critical and objective measure of the man and his work. In one other respect they are note-worthy; they treat of Freud not solely as the founder of psychoanalysis, but also as one who has affected the entire fabric of our intellectual, spiritual and aesthetic culture.

To the contributors of these essays, the Academy is much beholden. Their labors are in the best tradition of those who have made the Academy renowned, and their spirit, I feel certain, could not but prove congenial to him whose centennial they celebrate.

THOMAS C. PEIGHTAL, M.D.

INTRODUCTION

WE ARE here today to commemorate the birth of Sigmund Freud and his work. Freud revolutionized not alone psychiatry but many neighboring disciplines and had a marked and sustained influence on our whole culture. Freud furthermore is a unique figure among scientists. He remains until today in many ways a controversial figure. Usually a scientist and his works, after some years, are either accepted or rejected. But Freud continues to be—through some of the controversies which he created —a dynamic force. His concept of the unconscious, his libido theory, the stratification of the psyche, seen in dynamic terms, his deterministic and motivational interpretation of personality functioning, are still formulated, reformulated, confirmed and altered in our day. The same is true of psychoanalysis as a method of treatment and as a discipline of practical insight into interpersonal relationships and into social forces. Freud's contributions were not simply reorganized and then set aside, they continue dynamically to shape our thinking today. The appraisal and reappraisal of Freud's work will continue far into the future.

The Freud Centennial Committee of The New York Academy of Medicine has assembled a galaxy of essayists who will help us to understand and integrate Freud's influence on the sciences of human behavior.

PAUL H. HOCH, M.D.

New York
May, 1957

FREUD AND CONTEMPORARY
CULTURE

FREUD AND PSYCHIATRY

Kenneth E. Appel, M.D.

Chairman of the Department and Professor of Psychiatry,
School of Medicine, University of Pennsylvania

THIS IS an extraordinary occasion—this tribute to Sigmund Freud. It is a celebration and a commemoration. We are filled with great appreciation that such qualities—such generating perception, penetration and vision, such energizing and organizing capacity, should have come together in one man—catalyzing the culture of the century and our discipline of psychiatry. It has been given to few so to stir the minds of men and society and to make such contributions—Aristotle, Copernicus, Darwin and whom shall we select of the Nobel Prize mathematicians and atomic physicists? Einstein?

It has been a great gratification and inspiration to have shared in the enlightenment which Freud initiated.

Freud studied dissociated states: the phenonomena of the unconscious, the repressed, the indirectly expressed, the symbolic. In a manner not unfamiliar to psychoanalytic practice, in a kind of amphibolous fashion, I shall not concentrate alone on the intellectual, but shall address you in a dissociated way—with charts to stimulate your memories, your reveries and your free associations, while at the same time I will carry on a running account directed

3

to your cortex. Eugene O'Neil dramatized the hidden, amphoteric currents with masks and asides.

Several diagrams are presented for a coup d'oeil of the historical perspective in which psychoanalysis developed.[1]

TABLE 1—PSYCHIATRIC HISTORY

Lunacy	*Witchcraft*	*Astrology*
Torture	Thou shalt not	Royal Touch
Exorcism	suffer a witch to	Animal Magnetism
Burning	live	

Humanitarian Treatment

Pinel—1745-1828	Paracelsus—1493-1541
Tuke—1827-1895	Mesmer—1734-1815
	Braid—1795-1861
	Mesmerism = Hypnotism

TABLE 2—PSYCHIATRIC HISTORY

	vs.	
Charcot—1825-1893 Hypnosis = pathologic = only in hysteria		Liébeault & Bernheim Hypnosis = suggestion, not pathologic
Janet—dissociation, subconscious, psychological tension, psychasthenia		Bleuler—schizophrenia, autism, dereiam
		Meyer—Psychobiology
Freud—unconscious, sex, psychological mechanisms, psychoanalysis		Jung—libido, collective unconscious, psychological types, dementia praecox, functional disease
		Adler—inferiority, will to power, compensation

[1] For the thinking of an American at the turn of the century, see *The Varieties of Religious Experience—A Study in Human Nature* by William James, the Gifford Lectures on natural religion delivered at Edinburg, 1901-2. New York, Longmans Green and Co., 1916, pp. 207, 234.

TABLE 3—PSYCHIATRIC HISTORY

Suggestionists		*Persuasionists*
Babinski—pithiatism		Dubois—intellectual
Baudoin—auto-suggestion		
Coué—auto-suggestion		Dejerine—emotional

Kraepelin, 1856-1926
Classification, delineated concepts of dementia praecox
and manic depressive insanity

McDougall
Elaboration of instincts

Emphasis on functional point of view in Physiology and Psychology

Cannon	Wolff and Wolf	Rado
Pavlov	Ferenczi	Horney
Freud	Rank	Sullivan
Selye	Alexander	

Witchcraft derived from the Judeo-Christian tradition and appeared in man's inhumanity to man—persecution, torture, death. This was not confined to Salem. It remains in many of our institutions, current in much of our culture, ideas and activities, concerning the treatment (or absence of it) of mental and emotional illness. In addition to the humanitarian methods of Pinel and Tuke, a healing tradition developed from the concepts of the Royal Touch and Paracelsus' notions of the influence of the stars and the value of magnetism in healing. From all this one traces a line of development through Mesmer, Charcot, Liébeault, Bernheim, Breuer, Freud. Witchcraft is essentially hysteria. The Royal Touch, astral and magnetic influences, and Mesmerism were essentially hypnotism.

The contrast between psychoanalytic psychiatry and psychoanalysis is shown in several diagrams. Mapother as a representative of classical psychiatry presented the simplest modern classification of reaction types in non-analytic psychiatry. This represented an effort, a search, marked in classical psychiatry, to go beyond the descriptive and symptomatic levels to deeper, dynamic ones. (Mapother omits in his classification the repetitive, obsessive, psychasthenic type.)

TABLE 4—FUNDAMENTAL REACTION TYPES
Mapother

Syntonic {	Manic	Anxiety Neurosis
	Depressive	Neurasthenia
Confusional		
Schizoid		
Paranoid		
Hysteric		

Mapother thinks that neurasthenic conditions belong to the depressive syntonic reaction types, whereas anxiety states belong to the syntonic manic group.

Compare the simplicity of these conceptualizations with the abbreviated diagram of the Freudian Analysis of Sexuality (Table 5, p. 7).

Table 6 (p. 8) represents an abbreviation of Table 5.

Page (Table 7, p. 8) in *Abnormal Psychology* has constructed a diagram which incorporates the Death Drive with psychoanalytic theory. The dynamic relationships of the various aims and principles are represented. Page's scheme has seemed helpful in psychoanalytic orientation.[2]

These diagrams represent great complexity even in outline. But they give us a sort of map which enables us to orient ourselves in some of the personality and behavior

[2] Page, James L. *Abnormal Psychology*. New York and London, Mc-Graw-Hill Book Company, Inc., 1947, pages 1 and 6.

TABLE 5—FREUDIAN ANALYSIS OF SEXUALITY

LIBIDO or SEXUAL ENERGY MANIFESTS ITSELF IN:			
VARIOUS ZONES OR CHANNELS OF EXCITABILITY	Diffuse Body Sensitivity	warmth, infantile desires for comfort nirvana, playful purposeless muscle activity / ability to stand cold, athletic games, purposeful muscle activity	toward OBJECTS In succession:
	Oral	suck, swallow bite, devour	Own Body (AUTOEROTICISM)
	Anal	expel, reject, destroy retain, control	Own Ego (NARCISSISM)
	Genital	inspect, touch, masturbation marked aversion	Parents (HOMO-AND-HETEROSEXUALITY) (Latency)
and	Curiosity	inspect shame	Persons of Opposite Sex (HETEROSEXUALITY)
VARIOUS	Interest in Dirt	pleasure disgust, neatness	
IMPULSES	Interest in Smells	pleasure loathing	SOCIAL-IMPERSONAL-IDEAL OBJECTS (Scientific - Artistic - Cultural)
OR	Touch	over interest lack of interest	
MODES	Be Touched	passionate cold	
OF	Exhibition	immodest modest	
ACTIVITY	Aggression	cruelty, sadism, pity	
	Submission to Pain	suffer pleasure in pain masochism	
	Training and Education		

labyrinths of the human being. All this is not confined to the bizarre, the neurotic, the psychotic, the extreme, but is representative also to some degree of the normal. Some believe even these diagrams are too narrow, partial and specialized in that these psychoanalytic paradigms of human behavior present serious limitations. It is felt that

7

Table 6—EROS—LIBIDO

Organization and Development

Channels—Zones		*Aims—Functions*
Oral—Intake		Touch
Anal—Resistance		Feel
Hate		See
Social		Curiosity
Genital—Positive		
Relationship		
Friendliness		

Objects:

Body—auto
Self-narcissism
Parents—Oedipus
Castration
Gangs—Same sex
Homo
Adolescence—Hetero.
Marriage—Mate
Vocation
Society—Culture, Science, Art

Table 7—GENERAL BIOLOGICAL ENERGY

(Page)		
Eros or Life Drives		*Thanatos or Death Drive*
Libido Impulses guided by	Ego impulses guided by	Death and Aggression Impulses guided by
Pleasure Principle expressed by	Reality Principle expressed by	Nirvana Principle expressed by
Self love, love of others, uninhibited pursuit of pleasure	Satisfying needs of the body in socially approved manner. Use of sublimation and repression	Destructiveness toward others and toward self
Located in the Unconscious	Located in the Conscious and Unconscious	Located in the Unconscious
Represented by the Id	Represented by the Ego and Super-Ego	Represented by the Id

biological, chemical, cultural factors in the genesis of behavior should be recognized and emphasized. These outlines indicate the great perception, penetration and capacity for integration and synthesis of Freud, which few if any psychologists have approached.

Charcot, Adolph Meyer, Freud, all started as pathologists and moved from the materially and physically observable to the world of psychology. Meyer from his observations thought schizophrenia represented the accentuation of habits of withdrawal, exaggerations of maladaptive techniques in the face of life's problems and frustrations—in contrast to Kraepelin who believed toxic factors lay at the base of the condition. When I was a student in the early decades of the century, Meyer's classification with its very Greek terminology was much in ascendancy with its emphasis on the various ergasias.

TABLE 8—PSYCHOBIOLOGY
The Ergasias (Meyer)

Pathergasias	Abnormal behavior
Meregasias	Minor, part reactions Psychoneurosis
Holergasias	Whole reactions Psychosis
Thymergasias	Affective reactions Hyperthymergasia elation Hypothymergasia depression
Parergasias	Schizophrenia
Dysergasias	Deliria
Anergasia	Developmental defects

Freudian concepts gave us not only a more elaborate codification of impulses and behavior, but related clinical conditions to developmental stages of the individual, as shown in the following table.

TABLE 9—LIBIDINAL AND CLINICAL CORRELATIONS

Stages of Libidinal Development	Clinical Conditions
Genital stage	Normality
Phallic	Hysteria
Late anal sadistic—controlling	Compulsion neurosis
Early anal sadistic—destroying	Paranoid
Late oral—demanding exploring	Manic depressive
Early oral—dependent	Schizophrenia—stupor

A new rationale appeared in psychiatry. A new system of exploration was seen: disorders were related to developmental blockages, fixations, or regressions, rather than to changes in the brain, according to the premises of pathology long established in medicine since Koch, Virchow and Pasteur.

Basic Concepts of Psychoanalysis and Emotional Dynamics are represented in Tables 10 and 11.

TABLE 10—PSYCHOANALYSIS—*BASIC CONCEPTS*

The Unconscious
Basic importance of early developmental history and experience
Repression
Transference—Resistance

Freud's contributions may well be compared with those of Copernicus, Darwin and Newton. Copernicus removed the earth from the center of the universe; Darwin displaced man from the center of creation; Freud, following 19th-century physics, reduced man's personality to the mechanical dynamics of impulses and complexes. It represented an effort to make psychology and therapy reasonably mechanical and objective. Hence one may move un-

TABLE 11—PSYCHOANALYSIS—*ESSENTIAL DYNAMICS AND PROCESSES*

1. Painful, unpleasant experiences and ideas unacceptable to parents, custom, culture, religion are
    avoided
    rejected
2. Repression
3. Resistance to recognition and awareness
    Nietzsche:
    Memory says, I did this.
    Pride says, I could not have done it.
4. Dissociation
5. Unconscious—inclinations, preferences, aversions, fears, resentments, dependencies, prejudices, blind spots, handicaps, influence conscious thinking and behavior, still effective.
6. Childhood experience, impulses, untrained and antisocial, are important in adult behavior through shame, guilt, fear, reaction formations, displacements, sublimation.
7. Free association—road to the unconscious.
8. Transference—positive feeling to analyst gives patient security to expose, to unburden, to persevere and struggle. Negative transference, displacement, substitution. Inappropriateness, ineffectiveness of the personal and parochial in contrast to reality.

TABLE 12—CONCEPTS OF PSYCHOANALYTIC THERAPY

Free association
Abreaction
Transference :
              :
              : analysis
              :
Resistance   :
Interpretation of symptoms
                    dreams
                    phantasies
                    defense mechanisms
Uncovering and resolving major emotional problems of patient's childhood. Oedipus and Castration complexes. Fixation. Regression. Nirvana and Pleasure Principles vs. Reality Principle and Super-ego.

derstandingly to the age of anxiety and the loss of self-
hood, dignity and worth—through the destructive effects
of mechanization and hostility. Diego de Rivera has a ter-
rorizing mural of colorful mosaic, in a new hospital in
Mexico City, representing this process.

Newton discovered the pull of bodies, the force of
gravity. Freud directed attention to the "pull of the past,"
the importance of past experience in the functioning of
the individual, to childhood experiences and parent-child
relationships. "As the twig is bent, so is the tree inclined."
Freud's patient and penetrating observations with new
techniques revealed new significance in the conditioning
of the past, in the family and with the parents, in the
development and molding of adult behavior.

With the prism, Newton split white light into its com-
ponent wave lengths and colors. Freud saw the varieties
and distribution of human behavior and resolved them
into a spectrum of fundamental forces, forms, impulses,
motivations and mechanisms.

A diagram of the functional elements of the personality
according to psychoanalytic concepts is shown in Table 13.

TABLE 13—DIAGRAM OF PERSONALITY

Conscious Intellect
Ego
Mastery
Discrimination
Mediation
Perception

Instinct Emotion	*Social*
Id	*Super-Ego*
Fear	Standards
Hate	Expectations
Love	Identifications
	Oppositions

In addition to some of the concepts previously indicated, Freud introduced many terms and expressions describing behavior. They have become common in popular speech. The genius of Freud is shown in the great number of words and concepts which, through his observations and emphasis, have become part of the established vocabulary and cultural currency of our time. What other genius has had numerically such an influence on the language and thinking of a people? Aristotle?

Some of the most important terms, concepts and complexes are shown in the accompanying Table 14. In con-

TABLE 14—PSYCHOANALYSIS AND STANDARD PSYCHIATRY
Concepts accepted, questioned, rejected

Psychoanalysis	*Psychiatry*
1. Symptoms have psychological or emotional meaning and significance	Has generally incorporated 1 through 12
2. Unconscious	
3. Repression	*especially:*
4. Dissociation	
5. Indirect manifestation of impulse	Unconscious
6. Symbolization	Importance of *childhood* and family experience
7. Defense mechanisms	Repression
8. Structure of personality	Dissociation
id	Defense Mechanisms
ego	Transference
super-ego	Abreaction
9. Transference	Analysis
10. Resistance	Insight
11. Abreaction	
12. *Childhood and family experience*	
1. Oedipus and castration complexes	
2. Infantile experience	
3. Sexuality and libido	
4. Dream emphasis	
5. Free association emphasis	
6. Dream, symptom and fantasy interpretations	
7. Recovery of unconscious material	
8. Removal of infantile amnesias and study of universal infantile neurosis.	

trast to the dynamic, epistemic concepts of psychoanalysis, one recalls the descriptive, classificatory, delineating, relatively static concepts which have been part of standard psychiatry. One sees the concepts of psychoanalysis which have been incorporated into the psychiatry of today—down to and including Number 12 (Table 14). Concerning certain concepts there is much argument and disagreement—others are "excluded" by many thinkers.

Table 15 shows a translation or table of approximate equivalents of the terms of standard psychiatry of the first quarter of the century, and those of psychoanalysis.

TABLE 15—CLASSIFICATION AND TERMINOLOGY

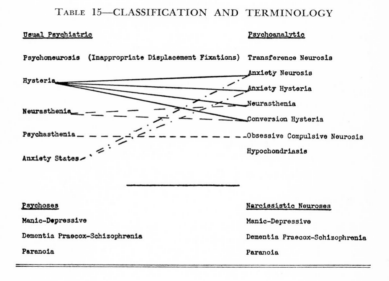

Usual Psychiatric	Psychoanalytic
Psychoneurosis (Inappropriate Displacement Fixations)	Transference Neurosis
Hysteria	Anxiety Neurosis
	Anxiety Hysteria
	Neurasthenia
Neurasthenia	Conversion Hysteria
Psychasthenia	Obsessive Compulsive Neurosis
Anxiety States	Hypochondriasis
Psychoses	Narcissistic Neuroses
Manic-Depressive	Manic-Depressive
Dementia Praecox-Schizophrenia	Dementia Praecox-Schizophrenia
Paranoia	Paranoia

For more completeness, Table 16 shows the Elements of the Super-Ego diagramatically, and Table 17 the Development of the Sense of Reality and the Ego.

TABLE 16—ELEMENTS OF SUPER-EGO

Parental influences: criticism, praise, authority, love, example, identification, reaction formation
Parental substitutes: nurses, teachers, employers
Herd opinion: religion, morality, esthetics
Hero worship: novels, history, newspapers, theatres, movies, friends
Conscious adaptation and development of a set of standards
Values—Expectations—Identifications—Oppositions
Conscience—Duty—Conscious Control

Psychoanalysis thus has pointed out and emphasized certain broad general concepts:

The push and pull of the past
The importance of development
The handicaps of development
The rationale of irrationality
The non-genitality of much of sexuality
The non-sexuality of much of sex
The extension of sexuality. The use of sexuality for non-genital goals
Sex is broadened to include sensuality, gratification, interest, cathexis, indirection, disguises, modification, symbolization of impulse, thought, communication, behavior, reaction formations.

TABLE 17—DEVELOPMENT OF REALITY SENSE OR EGO
(Ferenczi)

Unconditioned omnipotence (before birth)
Magical hallucinatory omnipotence (after birth)
Omnipotence by magical gestures
Power through thoughts and words
Perception, Discrimination, Evaluation, Mediation, between wishes of
Id and the Standards and Expectations of the
Super-Ego and the possibilities of
Reality
Mastery—Maturity—Problem solving

Kenneth E. Appel

It seems to me that unconscious, indirect, symbolic impulses and mechanisms (including physiology and chemistry) are underestimated in psychoanalytic therapy and psychotherapy and need to be more carefully investigated. Much of psychoanalysis in many quarters appears to be too formalized, rationalized, intellectualized and has become obsessive and compulsive. Much theory is built on a paradigm of 19th Century physics which is seriously questioned and apparently outmoded. Novelty, emergence, the creativity of new relationships and struggle are concepts that I believe psychoanalysis has underemphasized and which Kierkegaard, Maritain, Sartre, Tillich and the Existentialists have described as essential aspects of reality.

Out of years of painstaking labor, study and research in the laboratory, the dialectic of history, culture, science and circumstance moved Freud into the clinic. He made fundamental studies on the brain stem of different species of animals, significant observations on cerebral diplegia; he discovered the use of cocaine in anesthetizing the cornea for ophthalmic surgery. He had unlimited energy. He must have had the conviction of destiny—which his mother felt and the fortune tellers in the Prater fostered. He was brilliant in his studies. He came out of years of stern training in neurophysiology and neuroanatomy. He suffered the effects of loss of parental income when the Industrial Revolution deprived his father of his traditional work. He suffered the personal, cultural and professional persecution of the Jew. His young, warm and overprotective mother gave a vitality and security that his older, less appreciative, disciplining father threatened. The age of his father, the youth of his mother, the confusing family relationships—no wonder he had night terrors, enuresis and hallucinations! No wonder the Oedipus relationships

16

were strikingly delineated or etched in the apperceptions of this strong-feeling, determined, brilliant, unusual child. One shudders to think what would have been lost if Sigmund Freud had had normal personality reactions, normal family relationships, normal comfortable cultural and economic conditions and if he had had the comfort of what he desired in academic life under either Brücke or Meynert. Unreason, suffering, conflict (personal and cultural), disappointment, humiliation were numerous in the background of this genius. He was not a shaman nor a necromancer. He was a scientist and a seer. His hurts, humiliations and persecutions must have quite naturally built up a rigidity and compulsiveness to protect him against disruptive hostility. No wonder he seemed paranoid at times. The revolt of favorite pupils seemed to accentuate the amphictyonic league of the elect. But the very strength of the opposition was a sign of cultural vitality—a gain for society and culture. The strength of his feelings accentuated differences and dissidences which were psychiatrically and culturally valuable—as the emphasis on Ego psychiatry, cultural studies and anthropology have shown. The intensity of contrasts and opposition have stimulated supplementary thinking about heredity, constitution, physiological, chemical and neurological considerations, especially recently in connection with the newer drugs. I believe those who have strongly opposed Freud, even the organicists, have had their wits sharpened and have been stimulated to more enlightened perspectives and effectiveness.

Freud's life is shot through with irony. Anatole France, whom Freud admired, wrote in his *Garden of Epicurus* that irony is one of the universal themes and strands of life.

Kenneth E. Appel

The *volte face* in attitudes about psychoanalysis that took place in the course of Freud's lifetime was truly remarkable. Culpin[3] in his book has some quotations that are now almost unbelievable: "The psychoanalyst should be repressed with all the strength and force of a controlling hierarchy" (*Lancet, 1*:210, *1916*). Psychoanalysis is "exposed, blown up and discredited . . . its day is now past" (*Brit. Med. J., 2*:508, *1916*). Psychoanalysis is a "slimy, useless and offensive agitation of human sludge" (*J. Med. Scie.*, 692, *1916*). The psychoanalysts "are at their pernicious work in the lunacy wards of the great war hospitals" (*Brit. Med. J., 1*:64, *1917*).

However, in *1921*, a great change had taken place. Farquhar Buzzard in his presidential address to the Royal Society said, "Psychoanalysis is as necessary for the *study* of psychiatry as accurate patient history-taking is necessary for the elucidation of medical problems of organic origin." He quotes Bernard Hart, "It is certain that Freud's work has opened a *new era*[4] in psychology . . . and has *fertilized* immeasurably the arid field of old academic psychology" (*Proc. Roy. Soc. Med.*, Feb. *1921*, pp. 2-3). McDougall in *1936* writes (*Psychoanalysis and Social Psychology*, Wm. McDougall, Meitman Ltd., London, 1936, p. 17). "In my opinion Freud has, quite unquestionably, done more for the *advancement* of our understanding of human nature than any other man since Aristotle." This from the opposition and a critic! And in the *Journal of the American Medical Association* (Vol. *113, 1939*), on the occasion of his death, it was written that *"Freud discovered the most fundamental, dynamic fact of psychology—the fact of re-*

---

[3] Culpin, M., *The Nervous Patient*. London, Lewis and Company, Ltd., 1924, pp. 16-17.

[4] Italics here and in remainder of paragraph are present author's.

18

pression and resistance . . . *psychoanalysis has become firmly established* in psychology, education and in medicine."

Freud was a scientist and a seer. He was also a literary artist to whose ability Thomas Mann paid tribute. He was scientifically charismatic, but in the penetration and depth of his psychological ultra-microscopy, he missed at times the breadth of the lower power. He was unable to assimilate the divergencies of different perspectives. Another irony: he studied and defended individuality in his patients and in culture, but he could not accept it in his own psychoanalytic, cultural camp. He recognized difference and the importance of individuality, but often he could not recognize the value and obligation of dissidence, the reality of novelty, the inadequacy of determinism, the inevitability of change, the universality of it. Nor could he accept the impossibility of freezing life for long in rigidly mechanistic formulae, of making culture inflexible and have the personality survive. The constructive uses of individual perspectives, differences and dissonances were concepts he could not stomach. The iconoclast became the conservative of the next generation. This has happened in psychoanalysis. The amphictyony that has developed in certain areas of psychoanalysis is a matter of the greatest concern to educators and scientists. Freud's life stood for originality, novelty, rebellion. Yet some of his most faithful followers do not tolerate the spirit that generated psychoanalysis. Perhaps there is a cultural dynamic in this fluctuation and alternation of opposites. The spirit of Metternich has flourished, some have felt, more than that of Jefferson.

But let us not get stalled and hung up on doubtful and debatable details or parochial particularities. The view that Freud has opened up is illimitable, stimulating, and offers many directions in which to apply our energies. *There is no finality to thought or to science or to education.* A mountain has different outlooks and there are different roads to the top. Let not our narcissisms, defenses and wishes for omnipotence with consequent frustration set up obstacles to the progress to which the great psychoanalytic movement has pointed the way.

Psychoanalysis formed a ferment in the great masses of discouraged and apathetic patients and relatives. At first it was esoteric, almost cabalistic. It presented a challenge to understanding, once one had gotten over the initial startle and boldness of some of the suggested theory. Even to get one thinking in dynamic terms, in terms of psychological and social etiology, was a tremendous contribution.

The point is not the formulations and rituals arrived at, however neat, consistent and comforting they be, and not the relative disappointment in therapeutic results.

We must not get stuck on the incompleteness and fantasies and speculations; we must not be discouraged with the diversity of views and perspectives. These are healthy developments. The importance lies in the ferment psychoanalysis has stirred, the new look it has developed, the new perspectives it has presented, the roads and possibilities it has opened. We should not think of the past but the possibilities of the future and the future of research. Therefore the invitation to psychoanalysis to join the body of university scholars, scientists, educators, psychological and social researchers in all areas of human behavior should be accepted. Commemoration, yes—but also dedication to new directions and devotions. The incorporation of the past into the future which Allport indicates in his concept of "Becoming" is a challenge for psychiatry and psychoanalysis.

Psychoanalysis has engendered new beehives of activity —observations, notes, speculations, detailed records, infinite time with individual patients. Kettering has pointed to the importance of seeing something new where others have seen only the old. The new will come out of this hive of activity. The requirements of institutes, however rigid, have demanded time with patients, supervision and speculation. Good and valuable things are bound to result in spite of the rigidities, intellectual and professional castration threats and unquestioning convictions. Hope has sprung up in hospitals and in our communities from the analysts and their work. Analysis has brought light, sunshine, inspiration and hope into our communities more than into our hospitals. The results, as Dr. William Lhamon has said of this hedonic, motivational psychology, have not been as dramatic as penicillin for syphillis or nicotinic acid for pellagra or electricity for depressions, but the community and western culture are alive with psychiatry and psychoanalysis. Optimism toward the most discouraging psychiatric conditions is generated. Suffering people find analytic routines of therapy anxiety-relieving, even if not completely curative. Probably, therefore, suffering is lessened. A radical change of personality is not as frequently accomplished as one might hope, but as a result of the insights of Sigmund Freud, there is a new spirit abroad in psychiatry. The danger is that the radical empiricism of Freud will be displaced by authoritarian control of conservatism and the spirit of Freud will be lost.

The incorporation and integration of the energy and vitality, the enthusiasm and adventure of psychoanalysis into psychiatry and the science of human behavior, and into university functions, present untold opportunities for research, guided by the discipline of the scholarly tradition and the objectivity of the scientist. Psychoanalysis is not the millenium and is not the final word about human nature and psychiatry. It can, however, make still greater contributions if it becomes more closely integrated and collaborative.

The insights and contributions of Freud have been epochal. Before his time, psychiatry was classificatory, and treatment was expectant and custodial. Since his discoveries, psychiatry has become etiological and dynamic, and therapy rational, psychological and hopeful. His scheme of the development of the human personality has given us a paradigm by which we can understand much of the irrational, chaotic and bizarre, seen in psychiatric conditions. Freud himself changed his formulations and that process is still going on with progressive thinkers in psychoanalysis.

Many of the ten to twelve million patients in the United States with handicapping emotional disturbances cannot be analyzed—the majority of them for many reasons. But psychoanalytic insights are helpful in many conditions that cannot be analyzed. The psychoneuroses, some psychoses, and some psychosomatic or functional medical conditions, some character disorders and neuroses, are those in which it may be appropriately employed.

The insights of psychoanalysis far transcend its therapeutic efficacy. The contribution of psychoanalysis as a method of investigating the human personality, as a tool of research, and as a means of insight, may very well turn out to be a greater contribution than psychoanalysis as a method of therapy. But Freud's contribution has been basic. It has thrown light where there was darkness and confusion, and has brought order where we saw only chaos. It is comparable to the introduction of the benzene ring in organic chemistry. It has made our thinking functional and dynamic rather than static and verbal. It has given us new tools of thinking, understanding, therapy and cultural insights. It has opened new realms in psychotherapy and made it rational. The extravagances and errors of observation and theory will be corrected by time and experience.

The word psychoanalysis is used in a variety of ways, to designate different meanings. It is important to know in which sense the word is used in conversation or discussion; not all the meanings or uses of psychoanalysis are of equal value and acceptance. Its value as a means of obtaining psychological data is indisputable and accepted generally by classical psychiatry and psychology. Contributions in these areas have often transcended the other meanings. Popularly, the word psychoanalysis stands for a type of treatment or thinking, with a prognostic optimism, which records and results do not appear to justify. From this point of view much wish fulfillment is incorporated in the word. But psychoanalysis stands for life and action in the face of the frustration, pessimism and almost therapeutic nihilism and paralysis, which pre-dynamic

TABLE 18—PSYCHOANALYSIS—VARIOUS MEANINGS

A method of obtaining psychological data.
The collection of experiences or facts thus obtained.
A technique of therapy.
The various hypotheses or theories of psychoanalysis.
A philosophy of life or ethics
Designation used loosely for any one of the different schools.

and pre-analytic psychiatry offered to Public Health Problem Number One.

Many criticisms have been leveled at present-day classical psychoanalysis. Some say that as a therapeutic device its effectiveness is limited to a small number of patients highly selected economically and socially, because of the time and expense involved. In the professional lifetime of an analyst, he can treat only several hundred patients, whereas psychiatric conditions requiring treatment run into millions yearly. Many people who have been analyzed for years remain ill. The results of the different forms of analytic therapy appear to be statistically roughly the same. This seems to hold for any form of psychiatric therapy. Apparently the non-specific aspects of treatment are more fundamental than the intellectual frame of reference used.

It is claimed that the emphasis is too ritualistic and obsessive. The identical method unmodified is used with a great variety of very different psychiatric conditions and diagnoses. Psychoanalysis is too intellectual. There is too much insistence on the verbalization of insights, whereas the non-verbalized, unconscious aspects of therapy are underestimated and neglected. Making the unconscious conscious does not cure. Insight, of itself, does not cure.

It is said that there is too much stress on sex; that psychoanalysis preaches release of inhibitions and indulgence of instinctual gratification, too readily dispensing with super-ego controls; that it does not give adequate weight to moral, religious and social values.

There are those who feel that the conception of transference is too limited in classical psychoanalysis. It is not just a mirror to enable a patient to obtain a picture of events and patterns of personality development. It is not just a backboard upon which to discharge displaced feelings and recognize their inappropriateness and unrealistic nature or to learn of prejudices and handicapping impulses. It is not just to learn of the unconscious. It is not just to enable the patient to gain sufficient security to talk freely. The relationship with the therapist or analyst is not just a reproduction of important past relationships, but enables the patient to identify with a new point of view, with new attitudes revealed in the questions and manner of the therapist—an identification which is constructive, dynamic, enabling the patient to try the new, to experiment and acquire fresh, constructive impulses, attitudes and behavior.

Another criticism is that classical psychoanalysis is too retrospective and dwells too much on mistakes and liabilities, is not sufficiently oriented towards the future and the assets of the individual. It is too reductive and not sufficiently synthetic; too pessimistic and not sufficiently hopeful. It does not emphasize sufficiently faith, growth, novelty and the future. It is too individualistic. It does not emphasize sufficiency, the dynamic of "We-ness"—"Togetherness" and constructive identification. It is too Platonic, not sufficiently incorporating the insights of James and Bergson.

There are those whose criticisms are levelled especially at psychoanalytic theories in regard to the dynamics of human behavior. These are based, it is claimed, almost entirely on neurotic material and inadequate evidence, not statistically validated. Scientific methods are not used. Theories are based on retrospective reconstructions of the patient's productions and too frequently slanted by the analyst's special frame of reference. The processes of suggestion and intellectual direction are perhaps stronger

Kenneth E. Appel

than is generally recognized. Jung, Adler, Rank (and others) from the same observations reached different and at times opposing conclusions. It is said that the liberal analysts, like Alexander and Rado, in their modifications of psychoanalytic treatment are not really "doing" psychoanalysis.

The emphasis of psychoanalysis is too narrow, with a neglect of hereditary, constitutional, physical, organic, chemical, neurological, cultural and social factors. Theories were too much influenced by the presuppositions of now out-dated 19th-century determinism and the patriarchal culture of Vienna at that time. Much that psychoanalysis has taken as biological, others think is cultural.

As a movement, critics find psychoanalysis too dogmatic and authoritarian. Education of analysts tends to be indoctrination rather than the encouragement of original thinking and an objective search for truth. Whereas Ph.D. students in economics study not only Adam Smith but also Marx, the Physiocrats, the Mercantilists and J. M. Keynes as well, psychoanalytic students are not encouraged to evaluate other formulations of theory.

It is difficult to have an objective and open-minded critical discussion of psychoanalysis. No criticism is valid, it is claimed, unless a person has been analyzed, because he won't know what he is talking about. His defenses, his unconscious, his reaction formations and prejudices will cloud his evaluations. Those who have been analyzed usually become so completely converted that they have no criticisms to offer. There is a ready discounting of all criticisms. For example, if you deny the universality of sexuality and infantile neurosis, it is a defense against your awareness of their influence on your own life. If you get to an appointment early, you are anxious; if on time,

26

you are compulsive and perfectionistic; and if late, you are resentful and hostile. Where are you? You can't win. There is little room for normality; everyone should be analyzed.

Psychoanalytic institutes are too isolated from the currents of medical school and university life, traditions, practices and mutual criticisms. They are too removed from the company of scholars and scientists.

The above criticisms of psychoanalysis are of very varied and unequal importance. Some are emotional and defensive. Some are a result of misunderstanding. Some derive from inexperience. Some represent a "startle reaction" to new and tabooed material. Some are defensive of the traditional way of looking at human beings and society. Others do have a scientific and logical basis.

It is not within the scope of this discussion to enter into polemics. The contributions of psychoanalysis have been eulogized. This should not blind us to criticisms that will enhance its usefulness to psychiatry, psychology and society. Excesses and blind spots will be corrected by time, experience, discussion, reflection and the application of scientific and logical methods.

Criticisms are recorded here in an effort at completeness and perspective. Such a list is rarely compiled.

Parmenidean unity is comforting. But it is perhaps more of a consoling phantasy than Heraclitus' vision. Heraclitus may come nearer to biological, cultural and psychological factors in the observation of the flux of the many and the permanence of change. This is my reading of culture, science, and history. It is a lesson we must learn if the new vistas opened by psychoanalysis are to be adequately exploited and new tools of methodology and therapy are to be forged in the fight against the crippling and devastating effects of mental and emotional illness. Against the burdens and handicaps of the past, unwholesome training, atavism, unrealism and unwisdom, novelty, revision and change will take place in psychoanalysis. Whether it will take fifty years or a hundred years for psychoanalysis and psychiatry to be more effectively and wholesomely integrated remains to be seen. Certainly psychoanalysis, as we know it, will change.

I have attempted to present a picture of the relationships of psychoanalysis and psychiatry in the mid-Twentieth Century and pay homage to that great genius—Sigmund Freud.

FREUD AND MEDICINE

Roy R. Grinker, M.D.

Director, Institute for Psychosomatic and Psychiatric Research and
Training, Michael Reese Hospital, Chicago, Illinois

IN 1939, shortly after the death of Sigmund Freud, I wrote an essay in his honor entitled: "Reminiscences of a Personal Contact with Freud."[1] My closing sentence may be used to set the tone of this presentation: "Psychoanalytic science will be much more progressive and productive in the way Freud himself would have wished, if we do not deify him and deny him the human privilege of error." Freud himself was never satisfied and restlessly kept reformulating his theories and challenging new frontiers of the unknown as a great scientist would. He could not accomplish everything, even during his lengthy life span, but left to his followers much unfinished business which can only be completed if yesterday's ideas are considered as points of departure and not as fixed limitations.

In the intervening years since Freud's death only a few unbiased evaluations of his contributions have been made. Now that Ernest Jones[2] has courageously told the story of

1 Grinker, R. R.: Reminiscences of a Personal Contact with Freud, *Am. J. Orthopsychiat.* *10*:850-54, 1940.

2 Jones, E.: *The Life and Work of Sigmund Freud,* 3 vols. New York, Basic Books, 1953.

Freud, his life and his work, with friendly objectivity, perhaps it may be possible to evaluate the original psycho-analytic theory and methodology repeatedly, from the changing frame of successive decades of progress.

In participating in this centenary celebration of Freud's birth, I feel keenly the honor implied, but equally the responsibility of discussing more than those positive contributions which helped our medical ideas about health and illness. Indeed, I shall indicate what, in my opinion, are some of the areas of unfinished business and the modifications of psychoanalytic concepts and methods necessary for their contribution to even more progress in psychosomatic medicine. In this essay I shall discuss only Freud's influences without including later accretions from his students or followers.

One of Freud's earliest papers dealt with the somatic source of anxiety.[3] He postulated the notion that the blocking of libidinal expression, due to various influences that prevented sexual experiences, resulted in the transformation of libido into anxiety. This was a prototype, although not the first of its kind, of the influence of the soma on the psyche or a special *somatic-psychic* approach. As the years went by, Freud modified this theory of anxiety, although he never abandoned it. He continued to maintain that it was derived from a phenomenological approach in contrast to a more recent metapsychological theory. His last writings reaffirm that the source of those instincts which give mental expression to the id is in the somatic organization. Today we view lesser quantities of anxiety according to Freud's second formulation; as a function of the ego signaling the perception of future

[3] Freud, S.: *Gesammelte Werke,* 17 vols. London, Imago Publishing Co., 1941.

danger from internal sources and thereby setting into action a variety of preparatory defenses.

Although we do not now consider that anxiety is transmuted repressed libido, the phenomena and processes by which somatic disturbances express themselves during development in permanent ego deformations, or in maturity by creating peculiar affective states have become a subject of intense study. Destructive and disintegrating processes within the human organism are often experienced psychologically long before the medical man is capable of diagnosing or localizing them. For example, many individuals suffer from atypical psychological depressions and report dreams, the contents of which indicate a somatic malignancy, before this is apparent to other observers. We have lately become interested in the prophetic expression of impending death before tissue changes reveal the process to the physician.

Freud's most direct contribution to what we today call the *psychosomatic* field is found in a basic psychoanalytic principle developed from his studies of conversion hysteria. Repression of unacceptable emotional memories may be followed by bodily symptoms which symbolically represent what has been repressed, with a simultaneous punishment. Often a neurotic usurpation of somatic structures interferes with their physiological uses. In Freud's earliest writings we see few evidences that he considered that repressed painful memories could also interfere with the function of organs innervated by the vegetative nervous system, which seems to be the primary focus of psychosomatic medicine when that term is defined in a limited sense. He did recognize that many visceral disturbances constituted the "perceived effects" of anxiety, but in general he did not extend his concern with somatic experi-

ences beyond the tri-leveled oral, anal and phallic models
of instinctual expression. Physiological knowledge was not
far enough advanced to permit significant correlations
with the psychological understanding available from psychoanalytic studies.

Regression to infantile psychological patterns seemed
to revive not only all points of fixation, but also con-
comitant behavior and physiological activities of a less
mature order. Thus, the phenomenon of regression pre-
cipitated by the stress of conflict includes a change in
somatic functions. The form and content of symptoms re-
sulting from regression is usually understood on the basis
of Freud's concept of stages of libidinal development
linked to experiences with various bodily zones which
mature at successive ages. Intensities of satisfaction and
degrees of frustration facilitate fixation, and hence regression, in times of stress, and influence patterns of ego
function and content of self-images. Much clinical data
indicate that early infantile experiences, whether they be
positive in the nature of satisfactory relations with a
mother, or negative such as maternal rejection, childhood
diseases, or various restrictions of activity, have profound
effects on ego functions, self-esteem and growth potentials.
These carry with them throughout life the predisposition
for regression and disturbance of function.

Freud's contributions to the field of medicine also include more general influences. His continued and restless
search for etiological factors arising from past experience
of the organism was in great contrast to the search in his
time for specfic external bacterial agents, and to the naive
acceptance of constitutional-hereditary processes as being
singly the most significant etiological factors. However,
Freud also clearly recognized the limitations of psycho-

genesis. In several contexts, he indicated that psychology could not go beyond a certain point, and he hoped that cooperative biochemical or endocrinological explanations eventually might be forthcoming.

Finally, in his utilization of transference, which is the heart of psychoanalytic therapy, he reconstructed the doctor-patient relationship and formulated it in a new and scientifically understandable form. Although not explicitly utilized in the context that transference connotes in psychoanalysis, the transactions between doctor and patient can now be formulated and taught to the medical profession as important in all therapeutic relationships.

Freud did not fully commit himself to the psychosomatic approach, and by that I mean the need to consider that all functions in health or illness involve both psychological and somatic processes. Apparently after several attempts to apply concepts of physics and physiology, especially neurophysiology, to psychology, Freud concluded that there was no direct relationship between mind and body. Yet he often expressed the notion of lineal relationship as in the following phrases: sexual libido causes anxiety or repressed emotions produce paralyses. Jones explains these statements as shorthand not meant to be taken literally and comments that modern psychosomatists do the same. Thus Freud concentrated entirely on the psychological system since he was concerned only in interpreting its general laws of functioning by the technique of psychoanalysis. He insisted that psychological processes should be treated in the language of psychology, a basic principle which is often forgotten by those research workers who use physiological concomitants of emotions as indicating emotions themselves, hence making their psychophysical correlations impossible.

Freud's psychoanalysis thus brought man into clear focus as a natural unitary being as far as his psychology is concerned. He is both animalistic and rational, conflictual, past-directed and future-oriented, restlessly growing, learning and evolving new forms of social existence and propagating the old. These many facets are integrated in new and individual forms for each person by his organizing self-identity.

But after Freud's unsuccessful attempts to unify mind and body in any grand conceptual scheme, psychoanalysis tended to dichotomize man by isolating psychological concepts from biology. Its basic hypotheses of psychogenesis shifted emphasis away from biology and from the natural trend of science toward unified theory.

It is interesting that, although Freud worked almost entirely in the field of psychology, except for his early years, and did not promulgate any general principles applicable to the mind-body relations or to the psychosomatic approach, he always recognized the limitations of psychogenesis. Likewise his theories leaned heavily on constitutional strengths of the instinctual drives and of the ego's functions.

There is a tendency in any young discipline of science or medicine, when a man of genius has contributed the initial impetus and most of the conceptional framework, to continue operating with the original theories and methods. These are difficult to relinquish and are used as long as possible even though they may not continue to be fruitful as newer ideas and methods develop from tangential fields. To preserve the purity of a science or the uniqueness of a tool of investigation may not add more to the sum total of knowledge, but delay progress. Certainly maintenance of the authority of Freud's written words of yesteryear adds litle to his unquestioned place in the history of medicine, psychology and the humanities. I shall now enumerate briefly some aspects of psychoanalysis as applied to medicine that need modification.

1. *The search for single causes of illness.* This is an implicit concept because Freud often mentioned constitution and heredity especially in relation to the strength of the instincts but could do little with them by the method to which he consecrated his life. This his followers forgot. It is assumed that single causes were and are to psychoanalysis, psychological, although within that system the principle of multiplicity of causes is accepted under the term of "over-determination."

2. *The formulation of specific etiology* associated with nosological entities. Here too is an implicit concept which became the focal approach of large groups of psychoanalytic investigators in the psychosomatic field. For much too long a time, specific formulations were derived to explain so-called psychosomatic syndromes which lead to repetitive subtle variations of two basic themes: unsatisfied dependency and repressed hostility. The current research for specificity no matter how disguised as profile, character structure or vector processes is a one-cause concept.

3. *The possibility of cure* of those diseases in which psychogenesis plays a role in etiology. Freud often spoke of cures like any medical man of his era. Yet later he recognized that psychoanalysis was an inefficient therapy, rarely curing and at the best ameliorating illness. As the most rational available psychological therapy, its role in curing or worsening illness has not yet been evaluated carefully. Furthermore, the results of treatment are not adequate indications of validity of causal relationships.

Roy R. Grinker

4. *The theory of a mobile psychic energy* or libido, including derivative notions of sources, effects, quantities and displacements. It is interesting that Freud's "Project for a Scientific Psychology" emphasized quantity and energy in his early attempt to view physiology (neurophysiology) and psychology as unitary approaches.[4] This basic interest entered psychoanalysis via the concepts of libido and cathexis and has been perpetuated. We cannot envision at present how quantitative concepts can be tested by psychoanalytic methods alone. Even now analysts who do not accept the libido theory are viewed askance. Yet in our time we have become more interested in ego functions concerned in learning, and in their intimate connections with body functions in development and regression. From a libido theory corresponding to nineteenth-century biology we have moved to learning theory, organizing principles and the communication of information through signs and symbols depending on the level of organization in focus. We do not as yet know if these theories and hypotheses will prove more fruitful in psychology.

5. *The heavy emphasis on instinctual drives,* even though not to exclusion, has been maintained by analysts attempting to preserve in pure form the supposed true Freudian tool of investigation. As a result biological and sociological advances penetrate slowly and difficultly into psychoanalytic theory. But today instinct theory has become revived by the scientific investigations of the ethologists who study innate releasor mechanisms of primitive social responses in animals. The readiness to love and the

[4] Freud, S. Project for a Scientific Psychology. In: *The Origins of Psychoanalysis. Letters to Wilhelm Fliess, Drafts and Notes, 1887-1902.* New York, Basic Books, 1954.

displacement of aim and object gives validity to the part-role of instincts in personality theory.

It may be well in contrast to enumerate some current principles of the psychosomatic approach considered as part of modern behavioral science.

1. All functions of the living human organism, whether in health or illness, are psychosomatic.

2. All disturbances in human function are adaptive and involve multiple processes and causes.

3. Varying constellations of processes may find the same functional expression in a final common pathway.

4. The total human organism in varying interrelationships with other organisms and the material world and the part functions of any single human organism among themselves are viewed as transactional processes in fields of observer-defined extent.

5. Rather than utilizing the notion of psychic energy, we view relationships from the frame of reference of communications and the transmission of information. This is possible whether we are talking about social, psychological or somatic behavior.

6. The influence of strain on the organism differs with the phase of the developmental process or the state of regression at the time and that stress is the sum total of organismic response.

7. Heredity, constitution, strength of instinctual forces, life experiences with the first nuclear family and ever-extending social groups, precipitating factors, etc., are all important in the production of illness. Each has a place in the transacting field of strain and adaptation.

8. The organs that comprise the human body should not be isolated as single targets for a study of healthy func-

Roy R. Grinker

tion or illness for they are organized into open systems with highly permeable boundaries.

We should give great praise to Freud's *theories* for their profound effect on the progress of modern medicine in his time even though, as progress dictates, many are no longer fruitful. However, the influence of psychoanalytic *technique* on the psychosomatic field has contributed some impedance. This I should like to emphasize now as illustrative that time moves on and that the methods of medicine and science require change.

Psychoanalysis as it was applied to physiological disturbances remained as isolated as psychoanalysis in general from the other disciplines of science and medicine. Freud, the prototypic analyst, became isolated from medicine at the time when his first and greatest discoveries in psychoanalysis were communicated to the world. Many contemporary psychoanalysts insist that psychoanalysis continue to remain isolated with the justification that they are following Freud in preserving the purity of the method. Many others have broken with strict and slavish adherence to tradition and cooperate with other scientists; however, more are needed. The use of psychoanalytic techniques based on the body of psychoanalytic knowledge is essential for the observations of many aspects of psychosomatic illness which are not available through conscious reporting, and isolation of psychoanalysis is a deterrent to further progress.

Many individuals in the past have contributed a great deal to the development of the psychosomatic field by the use of the psychoanalytic method alone. In fact, the first formulations of specific unconscious dynamic patterns in medical syndromes were made by psychoanalysts using classical techniques. However, it is becoming increasingly apparent that this no longer suffices. Under such conditions of isolation no somatic examination or exact measurements of functions of organ or systems involved in a patient's disturbance, or those uninvolved in his complaints can be carried out. Significance is attributed to psychological data alone because of the method of observation, the focus and bias of the observer.

Without the synthesis of techniques of interview, psychoanalysis, and experimentation, the relationship between physiological processes and psychological functions cannot be established. I must state here that Freud personally opposed the experimental method in any relation to psychoanalysis with great vigor. He considered that each psychoanalysis was an experiment in itself, but that its low significance of reliability vitiated correlations with other experimental data. When we use one method alone, we are always confronted with the problem of determining to what depth in level in an individual, corresponding to past time, and to what particular somatic function we may attribute a relationship which constitutes the essential pattern of sickness.

The use of the psychoanalytic method for the treatment of the neuroses when transposed to psychosomatic research has resulted in unphysiological conclusions regarding regression, as if there were specific levels of psychological development at which only single zonal processes were significant and hence influenced by dysfunction to exclusion. Some, imitating the Freudian explanation of conversion hysteria, have considered vegetative symptoms as symbolic processes, even concluding for example that peptic ulcer represents a specific need or attack, or that it symbolizes a specific introjected object. Others have expressed the view that a physiological disturbance implies partial suicide based on the Freudian concept of the silent, internally operating, death instinct.

To round-out this presentation, I should like to point briefly toward current research in the psychosomatic field which takes cognizance of the vast body of knowledge and methodology developed by Freud, and utilizes as well as many other scientific points of view.[5] Current research is directed to the necessary understanding of laws involving the general relationships between psychological and somatic functioning before concepts of specificity of patterns may be developed. The need for multiple simultaneous foci of observations in multidisciplinary research, in which careful controls are utilized, is recognized. In every research, the field and time of observation and the methods utilized are carefully defined. The methods of observation utilize empirically logical systems and test variables that are suggested from clinical experience. Thus psychosomatic research today is transactional, which involves the study of relationship among many foci within a large field, not only in cross-section of current time, but also longitudinally in development from the earliest days of life. Current research is more concerned with general emotions or affects, either in isolation or in combination, than in specific dynamic states. These are definable and measurable and are more productive of correlatable information than the indirect quality of latent attitudes. Finally research today views emotions which are correlatable with significant bodily functions in health and illness, as conscious reportable experiences from the subject under observation. Psychoanalysis, as a tool specific to itself, may function in linking the unconscious repressed affects,

[5] Grinker, R. R.: *Psychosomatic research.* New York, W. W. Norton & Co., 1953.

which can be uncovered by its techniques, to what psychiatric studies reveal occurs on a conscious level.

Finally I should like to point out that widespread acceptance of psychoanalytic practice by the public helped popularize the psychosomatic field especially after World War II, but also demoralized psychosomatics as a science. The term "psychosomatic" has attained the dubious position of a household word. The stirring of interest in psychological medicine has resulted in a sacrifice of science to quick conclusions, although, in truth, the effect has been poor in sound results. The initial stimulus has been beneficial only to a point, for today our stereotyped psychosomatic formulations are largely conglomerations of vagueness. Now we should retrace our steps and relate psychodynamics to physiodynamics in a more scientific manner.

Because of my experience in the last twenty-five years, I can understand Freud's misgivings when I discussed the psychosomatic trend in this country in 1933 with him. He stated, "But that is the medicine of the future." Perhaps the second half of the twentieth century will be the future of which he spoke.

FREUD AND PROPHYLAXIS

Paul V. Lemkau, M.D.

Director of Mental Health Services
New York City Community Mental Health Board

I NEED hardly repeat the words of the preceding speakers concerning the honor one feels at being invited to discuss any one of the important issues at this centenary anniversary. To be tendered the honor of thinking together with you about Freud's relation to prophylaxis of psychiatric illness, the field to which I have devoted my professional life, is so flattering that I am afraid I accepted the challenge without thinking first of the responsibility that went with it. Such a lecture should come from a very thorough student of Freud's works who could quote incident, chapter and verse. I am not such a student and have never subjected myself to the vigorous study of the master entailed in training in a psychoanalytic institute.

I have, however, made a consistent search in Freud's writings for many years for references to prophylaxis. In the course of preparation for a paper, "The Implications of the Psychogenetic Hypothesis for Mental Hygiene," I wrote to a considerable group of outstanding scholars, some of whom share the honor of being on this program, asking them certain questions regarding Freud's concepts on prophylaxis. Freud made no direct mention of the problem so far as I have been able to find. We all recognize that he felt analysis much more an experimental, investigative procedure than a therapeutic or preventive one. He appears to have been concerned with the ever new vistas of his exploration, not with tidying up to see which of his new facts could be harnessed to the plebeian duties of the prevention of disease.

This fact leaves us with the rather delicate task of exigesis, drawing implications for one purpose from statements made and concepts used in other contexts.

Before proceeding to this task, it seems appropriate to examine briefly the general background of thinking about the prophylaxis of psychiatric illness and conditions. In the first place, there has been a great deal of confusion in the field because the all-inclusive concept "mental illness" has seduced scientific workers into a concept that there should be one prophylaxis for this unitary "illness." Realizing that there are probably as many psychiatric illnesses as there are recognized infectious ones, it seems far wiser to think in terms of the mental illnesses and of multiple methods of prophylaxis appropriate for each. Some of these are appropriate for discussion in connection with Freud; some are not. The prevention of hysteria with amnesia is a problem of prophylaxis to be discussed in relation to Freud; amnesia due to loss of brain substance, even though it be preventable, is not a matter of psychodynamic significance, Freudian or otherwise. This is true, even though it is clearly recognized that the precise nature of what is forgotten and how much is forgotten is of dynamic significance. So for the purposes of today's discussion, we are not concerned with the prevention of brain damage in the direct sense, nor with the results of brain damage.

Paul V. Lemkau

We are concerned with the prevention of the psycho-genetic mental illness and the behavioral complexes which are related to it and to the states of mind that lead individuals to expose themselves to risk of some sorts of brain damage (alcoholic, luetic). In other words we are concerned with the prevention of states of mind which are themselves illness or make the appearance of later illness all but inevitable.

It is popularly supposed that Freud believed that the past events in a life determined the presence or absence of illness at some future date. In an early "physiologizing" era, he did make such a direct cause and effect statement regarding some sorts of sexual activity and some types of anxiety. In general, however, the models Freud eventually developed were far more complex and dealt with so many vectors of force from so many different angles, from parent-child relationship to cultural influences, from aspirations to instincts, that the effect of any one could no longer be predicted. The analogies of levels, energy units to be satisfied, of checks and balances, of Eros and Thanatos, are so complex that the challenge to prophylactic adjustment of the forces and circumstances is avoided by most of Freud's followers. They even defend their position on theoretic grounds as though to indicate that therapy can cut these multi-stranded ropes but the same concepts cannot be used to cut the individual strands as the rope is being woven. A further problem is, of course, that Freud was not a systematist and had no intention of being one. He did not respond to a challenge to relate forces discussed at different periods of his own development to each other; he didn't think it worth while. I doubt that he would have tried to make a virtue of it, as have some of his followers.

The point I wish to make is that Freud did not directly discuss prophylaxis, and that to use his specific concepts systematically appears impossible. This being the case, we shall proceed to see what can be drawn from Freud's contributions that has been useful in the development of prophylactic programs in psychiatry.

Most of these ideas did not originate with Freud directly. Many critics and historians have pointed out that many of his ideas are older than himself, and that he himself used symbols going back to the earliest human thinking we know—such as the trinity of id, ego and super-ego. The modern movement of prophylaxis and of the promotion of mental health, however, considers Freud responsible for the following basic concepts. I leave to historians as to whether the attribution is justified.

First, it is proper to present an overall consideration that overrides any of the more or less specific points that will be made later. Freud's works and the popularization of his ideas, partly because his concepts were at first so fiercely attacked, induced an era of thinking in terms of the psychological meaning of life events that has furnished the soil in which ideas about the prevention of the psychogenic mental illness could grow. He furnished the multitude of hypotheses that arrested the interest of not only medical men but of many other people as well, not only professionals and the educated, but a considerable proportion of the total population. The population for the most part, I suspect, had little or no idea of what Freud's basic philosophy was; this made no difference for he was the symbol for the psychological interpretation of events, and this idea made a very great change in the scientific milieu. Out of this milieu grew the hopes and the hypotheses of prophylaxis in psychiatry.

Fundamentally, this movement has had within it more optimism than its Freudian origin would seem to justify. Freud did not speak much of constitution which had been the pessimistic concept that had dominated psychiatric etiological thought before him and of those who opposed him strongly early in his career. But, to some extent, his acceptance of the idea of instinct is also a pessimistic idea not much removed from constitutionalism; it is really but the analysis of a general, nonspecific concept to its more specific and more clearly characterized parts. Instinct is in-born and its forces are set more or less outside the control of the individual concerned. In this sense, the popular concept of optimism about psychoanalysis as a form of treatment is almost a perversion of what appears to have been Freud's genuine attitude. It is interesting, at least as I observe the situation, that in this country, Freud's pessimism dominates many of his followers' thinking about the possibilities of prophylaxis, while they seem quite sanguine about the use of his concepts and technics for curative purposes, an attitude I was impelled to complain about in the paper referred to earlier.

The first generalization is that behavior is caused in every instance, that no significant action or reaction occurs without antecedent events that determine it. Early in the Freudian period, the relations seemed rather clear, but as the structure was built up, individual events seemed to lose importance until many workers took the pessimistic view already described.

Suffice it to say that the hypothesis of psychologic determinism seems fundamental to any prophylactic program in psychiatry. If we are working in the psychogenic illnesses in a field of random concatinations of events with no predictability, then prophylaxis is certainly impossible.

Freud attempted to make illness and illness-precipitating states understandable, and, to some extent, predictable. What can be predicted in human living can probably be influenced to alter that predictability. Freud was not the only person of his time to insist on such a concept. The idea is basic in the psychiatry of Meyer and other leaders as well. But it is to Freud that cause and effect relationships seemed so clear that his writing "sold" the idea into public acceptance. Actually, Freud only interpreted past events; he nowhere said, "had this not happened, this later event would have been a healthy rather than an unhealthy reaction." The movement in the direction of prophylaxis of psychogenetic illnesses has acted as though he had meant to make the statement; as such, the effect of the non-existent statement has been extraordinary.

The second and genuinely basic contribution of Freud is that behavior matures from infancy to adulthood. I do not propose to discuss the various parameters of development Freud uses at different times and for different purposes, but to confine the discussion to the fact that he knew the person to be different at different stages of development. The infant was different from the school child and the adult. The attempts to pin the idea down using such terms as oral, anal, and genital states, the homo- and hetero-erotic stages, the various complex situations such as the Oedipus, do not always come out into consistent patterns. So far as I have been able to discover, Freud never defined what was a healthy resolution of the Oedipus situation or how the resolution could be led to a smooth and healthy end. I have also felt that Freud, but particularly some of his later followers in child analysis, have failed to recognize that the intellectual and sensory capacity of the brain matures also, along with its relationship capacity. Failure to recognize this has led to the assumption of far more complex kinds of relationships and numbers of items in a child's conscious and unconscious than there is capacity to entertain at the particular stage of development under consideration.

All of these questions do not detract from the basic concept that there is a maturational pattern and that events can change the way the pattern works itself out. This is, of course, something people, writers and the common man have known for centuries. Its implications for mental health, however, must be ascribed to Freud and his influence.

The next essential factor in prophylactic theory that arises to prominence because of Freud is a derivative of that just discussed, namely, that the individual not only matures but that he follows a more or less predictable course in the maturation; that is, one stage forms the basis for the predication of the next series of behavior patterns. Contributions to the idea from animal psychology and child development researches have certainly been fundamental in development of the idea since Freud made it current. The concept is very necessary, however, in the short term evaluation of all preventive efforts; in the absence of such progression one must await the passage of many years before the effect of a procedure can be evaluated. If behavioral progressions can be established firmly, the time of movement from one to another step may offer a way to evaluate progress or lack of it. Orderly predictable stages in maturation of infant to adult behavior is a Freudian concept important to the theory of prophylaxis.

The next concept basic to prophylactic work as regards

the psychogenic illnesses is that all individuals will have to go through certain experiences and that these will be more or less stressful. Perhaps the best example is that of the Oedipus problem. Freud contended that all had to live through it. In Freud's mind, most of the important developmental situations dealt with were intensely personal or familial problems and situations. Others gave a much broader definition of the steps before the infant. The students of development speak in terms of motor and sensory developmental "tasks." Meyer and particularly his student, Cameron, were concerned with a whole range of roles to be learned; Sullivan, with interpersonal relationships to be mastered. The educational psychologist studies what situations the child may be expected to master at a given age or stage of development. It appears that the germ of the concept of seeing maturation in terms of tasks to be surmounted and roles and relationships to be learned is justifiably attributed to Freud. The way particular developmental tasks are surmounted has offered the bench marks of evaluation that have made possible the programmatizing of prophylactic efforts.

The next great idea for prophylaxis that flows from Freud's thinking is that the factor of relationship with other people is important in personality development. Put in figurative language, one might say that the furnace in which the gold of personality is refined is that of interhuman relationships. Here again, there is real doubt whether Freud actually ever thought of the problem in this positive sense for he was more concerned with pathology, even the pathology of every day life, than he was with the possible prophylactic character of relationships. It is but a step, however, from the clearly Freudian concept that pathological relationships cause pathology to the concept that healthy relationships cause health, whether or not Freud himself ever took this step.

The *quality* of the effective interhuman relationship was much more the subject of enlightenment by Freud. Perhaps starting from one of the most important of his discoveries, the factors of transference and counter-transference in therapy, Freud was able to describe the force as well as the content of many parent-child relationships and of relationships between peers as well. Out of this work has been evolved a great deal of the modern educational thinking about motivation and its cultivation, as well as the recognition and the management of resistances to learning. Freud dealt with these matters primarily within the spheres of psychopathology, but the way he dealt with them has made possible the development of much of modern educational technique. In this sense, the whole movement of group dynamics has its roots in Freud's recognition that all ideas have emotional auras and that changing ideas always involves changing sentiments or attitudes, emotional sets.

In pointing to the overweening importance of the parent-child relationship, Freud opened the door to fitting mental health thinking into the pattern of prophylactic theory that was growing contemporaneously in the public health field. It was his work that made possible the analogy between early immunization and early behaviorial prophylaxis. Time may possibly prove that the analogy is a false one, as experimental tests have tended to show that many specific points of his doctrine do not correlate with observable life experience. This will not detract from the tremendous importance of the concept in the history of science, not only psychological medicine, but the social sciences as well.

The final contribution of Freud to prophylactic theory and practice that I wish to discuss is his concept that the culture in which an individual lives makes a difference and has meaning for the *individual* as well as for the group. Freud's contribution to anthropology is discussed by another in this symposium. Suffice it to say here that it appears that much of our present expansion of health so that it includes mental and social well-being as well as physical intactness can be traced to the pregnant ideas of Sigmund Freud.

There are those, I am sure, who will point out that I have ascribed to Freud things which rightfully belong to other minds. There are others who will say that Freud is directly responsible for far more of present prophylactic thinking than I have given him credit for. I regret that I cannot debate with either camp on the basis of expertness in Freud's enormous literary out-put. I can, however, defend my views as an interpretation by a person who has for a considerable while been concerned with the problem of prophylaxis of mental illness and the promotion of mental health, and as one who has tried to find the origin of current concepts in the field.

In summary, Freud, in my opinion, contributed the basis for the following fundamental tenets in prophylaxis:

1. Behavior is caused and the causes may be modifiable so that undesirable behavior may be avoided.

2. There is a maturation of emotional reaction.

3. That this maturation process is orderly and to some extent predictable.

4. That development involves stress, a concept economically expressed in the idea of developmental "tasks."

5. That the maturation of the personality takes place in and is modified by emotionally significant relationships, and that parent-child relationships are of great moment.

6. That the culture makes a difference and has meaning for the individual as well as for the group.

FREUD IN THE PERSPECTIVE OF MEDICAL HISTORY

Gregory Zilboorg, M.D.

Clinical Professor of Psychiatry
University of the State of New York

T HE figure of Freud stands out against the background of medical history as so different from any of the great men of his or of our generation that in order to understand this singular fact it is necessary to take cognizance of the historical changes of which Freud's and our generation were witnesses as well as victims.

All great men were great because in one way or another they were ahead of their time; or, to put it a little more correctly even though more bluntly, their contemporaries almost always welcomed them into history with irony, sarcasm, derision, at times slander, and quite often defamation. One would want to assume that the nineteenth century and our own were a little more enlightened, and were able to recognize a man's greatness more readily and with more tolerance than the sixteenth century that hounded Paracelsus into poverty and even into untimely death. Unfortunately, our assumption, if it were made, would not fully stand the test of actual events. Suffice it to recall the attitude of the medical world toward Lister and "Listerism" at the dawn of antiseptic surgery. His was a hard road to medical fame, even though his fame became long and great during his own lifetime. The derision with which Pasteur was temporarily rejected after his views had once been accepted by the Académie is well known.

However, this must be said of the latter half of the nineteenth century: The Franco-Prussian war, like many other wars having settled nothing, brought about an illusion of enlightened peace, and for a little over a generation the European scene became calm, sedate, earnest and conservative. The liberal had an argument to hold, not a fist fight to start, with the conservative. The revolutionaries, who only yesterday had dominated the French Commune, led by anarcho-communists, quieted down, while the Marxian socialist became for a while a student, a bookworm, a dreamer within the framework of parliamentarian and quasi-parliamentarian Europe. The ferment of social and political revolt was shifted backward to Russia, whose revolutionary emigrés and refugees enjoyed their liberty in London, Berlin, Vienna, Zurich and Geneva, busy preparing the social revolt in Russia. The center of international political contentions also moved east—toward the Balkans and parts of Northern Africa. There was something of pedestrian fatigue yet cultivated creativeness which mid-Victorian England, united Germany under Prussia, Franz Joseph's Austro-Hungarian Empire, and the French Third Republic had in common.

The intellectual climate of Europe favored the establishment and crystallization of the scientific method, and it invigorated and perfected the efficiency of medical practice and the ever greater fruitfulness of medical research— primarily in pathology and physiology and organic chemistry. The great medical men found on the whole a congenial and friendly unity and a sense of fraternity among themselves—all this despite the historical tradition of putting a few barbs into the garlands which were offered the newcomers who were destined to become great.

What could be more moving than that scene in the University of Paris, in which the aging Pasteur, leaning on the arm of the President of the French Republic, listened with ill-controlled emotion to the words of greeting uttered by Lister (not yet a Lord) in the name of the Royal Society. And at the time of his death Lister had already become the proud possessor of medical and nonmedical honors; he had received the Prussian Order *Pour le Mérite* as well as the Order of Merit (he was one of the 12 who received the order at the time Edward VII founded it). Medical scientific progress knew no political or ideological borders, and the men who carried on this progress were honored by governments as well as peoples.

To be in politics did not mean to be excluded from scientific work. Virchow, for instance, an opponent of Bismarck, was a liberal deputy in the Imperial Reichstag. Some 50 years earlier in the youngest of the republics, in the United States, one of the founders of the American Psychiatric Association, Dr. Stedman, was a member of the Senate of the Commonwealth of Massachusetts. A little over 100 years before, one of the signers of the Declaration of Independence, Benjamin Rush, proved also to be the founder of American clinical psychiatry and the author of the first textbook of psychiatry in America. Old Europe and the New World's great public lived scientifically in unison. It was the American Oliver Wendell Holmes who suggested the term "anaesthesia," which was universally accepted. The great clinical traditions of America and

Europe became one unified and mighty creative medical organism.

The eighties and the nineties of the past century represented a unique picture of steady progress and greatness of medicine in all its branches. There was the American Austin Flint who died in 1886, the year when Freud began his private practice in Vienna; there was James Marion Sims who died in 1883, a year after Emil Kraepelin (whose centenary of birth is also marked this year [1956]) started his work in the Flechsig Clinic in Leipzig. Brown-Séquard died in 1894, the year after Freud wrote his first psychological paper "On the Psychical Mechanism of Hysterical Phenomena." Helmholtz, under whose influence Freud's thinking turned toward a number of analogies from physics, also died in 1894, as did Oliver Wendell Holmes, the year Freud wrote his "Defense Neuro-Psychoses." E. Du Bois-Reymond, whose thinking and influence in the field of medicine and biology equaled that of Helmholtz, died in 1896, the year Freud wrote his articles on "Further Remarks on the Defence Neuro-Psychoses." Thomas Huxley died the year before, when Freud wrote "The Psychic Mechanisms of Obsessions and Phobias." Only one year later Roentgen pictures were first used, in the Greco-Turkish war.

We will not forget the famous "four doctors of Baltimore." Lister and Pasteur have already been mentioned. Koch was at the height of his career; and Klebs, the German physician, became professor in the Rush Medical School in Chicago in the same year (1897) as the first X-rays were used in the Greco-Turkish war. Our own Adolph Meyer moved east from Illinois to Worcester State Hospital to start a great career as a teacher of psychiatry. It was in 1900 that Klebs returned to Europe; in the beginning of that same year Freud's "Interpretation of Dreams" appeared.

By the listing of the great number of names already mentioned the galaxy of the great is not exhausted. Darwin, for instance, who died in 1882, should not be overlooked. Griesinger, Daniel Hack Tuke, Maudsley, Charcot and Pierre Janet cannot be forgotten, as Liébeault and Bernheim, the great masters of hypnosis under whose direct influence Freud once was, cannot be skipped.

Yet it is not a matter of names. The point is merely this: in whichever direction we look, we find that the general picture of medicine, including psychiatry, at the time Freud as a young physician started his practice, was that of a scientific extension of the modernized principles of Hippocratic medicine. Pathology and surgery, physiology and medicine were welded together into a system of thought and practice which conceived a man as a complex biological apparatus subject to the laws of physics, chemistry and certain general biological principles which presented a sort of blend between the biological philosophy of Darwin, the cellular pathology of Bichat and Virchow, and the biology of microorganisms, and the physics and chemistry of the day. *De facto,* if not in theoretical structure, medicine envisaged man as a wonderful machine almost in the Cartesian sense, the proper functioning of which meant health, and the dysfunction of which or the breakdown of certain of whose parts meant illness. The breakdown of course might be produced by various factors within or without the human organism. Illness on the whole, whatever its causes, meant a failure of certain organs. The restoration of these organs to their normal functioning, or their removal from the organism if such a removal did not mean death of the organism, meant successful treatment.

With certain exceptions, and at times significant exceptions, to the contrary (like a Liébeault, or a Bernheim), psychiatry was not considered different from any other part of medicine. The diseases which this branch of medicine embraced were considered diseases of the brain, of the central nervous system. These diseases had their course; their cerebral pathology, even though not as yet demonstrated, was taken for granted. Hence the great Hippocratic system of symptomatology, course and prognosis which the psychiatric sibling of Freud, Emil Kraepelin, endeavored to create. Experimental medicine in the best sense of the word of which a Claude Bernard made us think, organic pathology in the best sense of the word of which a Virchow made us think, the neo-Hippocratic clinical principles of observation which were in the best tradition of a Sydenham, were the principles of the day.

When Freud started his medical career, he was imbued with this tradition. In Brücke's laboratory he even followed it faithfully, but already he seemed to be looking elsewhere. As far as seeking proper training in order to get ready to practice and gain a livelihood, Freud seemed to follow the traditional path; from the standpoint of medical clinical mannerisms, he seemed to be a gifted, conventional young doctor who wanted to make a living and a name for himself. But very early in his career, at any rate by the time he went to Paris to study under Charcot, and shortly afterward when he returned to Vienna and started to work with Joseph Breuer, Freud showed definitely that he was a sort of dour maverick on the horizon of medicine. Eager, ambitious and restless, with more than a mere tendency to be quite tense, anxious and a little willful, he seemed to be what is labeled by that platitudinous, so full of meaning and yet indefinite, adjective known as "different."

Particularly in retrospect we can now see that Freud in one way or another paid merely verbal tribute to the physicochemical pathophysiological tradition of the medicine of his day. In actuality he seemed to be busy looking elsewhere and seeking something he knew not what. Intuitively, but not yet clearly, rationally and objective, he sensed that he was going in some new direction which destined him to take a unique place of his own in the history of medicine. This feeling expressed itself in his occasional but pithy references to the effect that he was going to be a great man, that his future biographers would have a difficult time in writing his biography. He enjoyed in advance visualizing their difficulties when as a young man, not yet married, he would destroy his personal papers so as to puzzle the future historian of medicine who would want to write his biography!

To assume today, one hundred years after Freud's birth, that a definitive biography of the man and a proper evaluation of his place in medical psychology are already possible is to assume the impossible. It is true that Freud was born one century ago, and that many striking changes have taken place during this century. But the work of Freud is too complex, the various components of it are so contradictory in relation to each other inwardly or outwardly, his work is so far from being a truly organized system, that from the standpoint of historical method and tradition it would be foolhardy to attempt to formulate today a systematic medicopsychological evaluation of Freud and of the place of psychoanalysis in relation to the general currents of medical history. It is true that Freud was born 100 years ago—but one should not forget that he died only 17 years ago. It is true that the Freudian revolution gave psychoanalysis a world-wide reputation and made it a byword of some sort of greatness as well as of some sort of fad. It is true that the future of Freud is probably not that of a Mesmer in the history of medicine. Yet it is also true that the passions around psychoanalysis are still raging, and that the calm, serene atmosphere of research in the manner of pathology and physiology does not seem at hand, as far as psychoanalysis is concerned. Yet again, here is a paradoxical phenomenon. Kraepelin, the great systematizer of clinical psychiatry and the founder and leader of scientific psychiatric research of the nineteenth century, Kraepelin whose hundredth birthday is also being celebrated this year, is hardly mentioned anywhere. In February, 1956 a special scientific celebration marked the Kraepelin centenary in Munich; but nothing was done about it in France, and the 1956 annual meeting of the American Psychiatric Association—which is conservative both professionally and scientifically—takes part in the solemn observance of Freud's centenary of birth but Kraepelin seems to be passed over unnoticed. Nor are there any signs that Eugen Bleuler, the other illustrious psychiatric contemporary of Freud, whose centenary falls in 1957, is being given any particular attention. Even the greatest contribution of Bleuler, his volume on the schizophrenias, waited thirty years before it was translated into English, while Freud's complete works are already published both in English and German, and both in England. As early as 1922 the complete works of Freud were being published in a Spanish translation in Spain.

We may speculate about this popularity of Freud and the controversies which he aroused, thus calling the attention of psychiatry to psychoanalysis more vociferously and more often. These purely external aspects of the Freudian controversy and popularity are not sufficient to explain the particular hold which Freud has on the psychiatry and medicine of today. After all, whether we deal with what people mistakenly call classical psychiatry, or such hybrid derivatives as psychosomatic medicine or child guidance or mental hygiene, all these branches of medical psychology give signs of being profoundly influenced by Freud—whether full, or partial, or no credit at all is ostensibly given to Freud by any of the workers in these branches.

A historian dealing with the positive aspects of the evolution of modern medicine must of necessity leave out, for the time being, Freud's controversies with religion, morality or general philosophy, or even his methodology. Time and the natural course of scientific growth will quiet down the controversies and will separate the chaff from the wheat. It is true that the popular misconceptions of Freud's ideas on sex, and the universal propensity to make the quasi-lurid more lurid and the quasi-sensational more sensational made Freud's name almost a common noun. But I doubt that the features of psychoanalysis dealing with sex, and the universality of such catchwords as the Oedipus or castration complexes (to the average man these are no more than catchwords), or Freud's assertion that Moses was an Egyptian and religion is a compulsion neurosis—I doubt whether these things played a decisive role in psychoanalysis having exerted such a telling influence on medicine and leaving in such a short time such a deep imprint on the total picture of contemporary medicine and medical history.

May I therefore offer the following for your consideration:

If we wish to find one single, unifying principle that motivates the practice of medicine, the art of healing, the striving to cure, the craving to combat human disease, we shall strike not very far from the mark if we say that this principal is not so much human curiosity, or the striving for personal self-preservation, as that simple human attitude of compassion for the sufferer, that natural and almost automatic albeit anxious ability of man to put himself in the place of the other person who is afflicted with an illness, It is, to use modern psychological terminology, our natural, automatic identification with the sufferer. In the beginning this identification may act only on cases of those illnesses which we might consider or fancy as curable. We want to *cure* our fellow men. The possible admixture of selfishness in the process (we cure ourselves as it were by curing others) may be disregarded, since this is a refined, psychologically and morally heightened selfishness—for the psychological borderline between ourselves and our suffering fellow men has become invisible in the process of transforming the simple human being into the bearer of that spiritual quality which we might call medical charity.

Whatever the spiritual implications of this process, the psychological process is that of the automatic unconscious identification with the patient. The average man goes through the same psychological processes, and on the scene of medical history he acts through the physician whose skill must equal his charity. I am inclined to imagine that at first this was true, as I have said before, of those illnesses which did not produce permanent deformities. A cripple, a leper, required a much greater evolution in

the direction of charitable identification with the ill. Even
St. Francis of Assisi had to make an intense effort not to be
revolted by the leper, and not to turn and run away from
him. In our own time tuberculosis used to evoke a reaction of fear and flight and disgust—until we learned
that we could cure tuberculosis. And today we are wit-
nessing a gradual change in a similar direction as far as
cancer is concerned.

Man has great psychological difficulties when he is
called upon to identify himself with someone who seems
permanently afflicted, hopelessly doomed. The mentally
ill were considered for centuries such hopeless creatures.
No wonder that the average man as well as the medical
man kept his face turned away from the large masses of
the mentally ill, sometimes in disgust, sometimes with
open hatred, sometimes in mortal fear. To identify one's
self with a psychotic, or even with a neurotic, was almost
impossible, and even today it is quite difficult or impossible at times.

It is in this sphere of psychological functioning that
Freud, not suddenly, of course, not without predecessors—
nothing in history is sudden and totally independent—
stands out as having made an enormous and unique contribution. It is true that the hope at first held out for the
cure of neuroses by means of psychoanalysis did not prove
as fully justified as the original enthusiasm seemed to
promise; even Freud himself avowedly lost to a great extent his faith in the complete curative efficiency of psychoanalysis. While all this is true, Freud's contribution remains
incontestable and immense. It is what it is because in the
scientific climate and tradition of the medicine in which
Freud was nurtured, and on the historical medical background from which Freud stepped out to the forefront

of medical psychology, human, clinical psychology was more or less excluded. And while Freud spoke in physico-mechanistic terms, because that was the scientific tradition and language in which he had been trained, in actuality he promulgated almost unwittingly an old, almost eternal truth which had theretofore escaped clinical medical tradition; he promulgated (it took him nearly a quarter of a century to do so) the belief that the average man, the so-called non-neurotic man, the every-day man, functions "normally" on the level of the psychopathology of every-day life; that the psychological laws governing our unconscious, affective life are equally valid for all men, the mentally ill and the mentally healthy; that these laws are not violated in health or in disease any more than the laws of chemistry or physics are different in physical health or physical disease.

In other words, Freud opened the road for a proper psychological identification with the neurotic and psychotic—an identification not based on anxious intuitiveness, on some sort of sentimental philanthropy or pity, or on a sociological utilitarian goal, but an identification based on an actual psychological equation between ourselves and the mentally ill. It is this identification, as I pointed out above, that opened wide the path to what I have called medical charity.

Among the paradoxical aspects of this great influence of Freud is the claim that he was fully detached, objective, disinterested, above the battle. He was not, of course. But it was Freud nevertheless who completed the great historical process of reuniting on a scientific basis, or in scientific terms, the body and the psychology of man. It was a singular synthesis of the early influences of Hughlings Jackson and Brentano. Whether Freud called his field the psyche, the soul, the spirit, the mind, what he actually described and dealt with was the psychic apparatus—his own scientific construct which appears to be more in harmony with man's normal and abnormal behavior.

In other words, the concept of the indivisibility of the human personality was reestablished within the realm of medical science; theretofore, this indivisibility had been recognized only by the religious, and particularly the Christian, concept of the human personality. The terminology remained and in many quarters still remains confused, because the differentiation between the medico-psychological concept of the psychic apparatus and the theological concept of the soul has not yet been fully recognized in many quarters. But if we bear this differentiation in mind, we shall be able to appreciate the magnitude of Freud's contribution to medicine and to psychiatry, to each of these separately and to both jointly. If we bear also in mind the reservations with regard to terminology, we may feel that Freud met fully the criticism of medicine which Plato uttered almost twenty-four centuries ago, saying: "For this is the great error of our day, that physicians separate the body from the soul."

THE IMPACT OF FREUD ON ANTHROPOLOGY

Clyde K. Kluckhohn, Ph.D.

Professor of Anthropology, Harvard University

ALTHOUGH psychoanalysts turned their attention to anthropological data as early as the first decade of the nineteenth century, psychoanalysis has had a serious influence upon anthropology for only (roughly) the past twenty years. The first reactions of anthropologists were largely negative.[1] Indeed, to this day the impact outside the English-speaking world has been either casual or negative or both.[2] British interest in psychoanalysis was relatively early because of a psychologist turned anthropologist (W. H. R. Rivers) and a physician turned anthropologist (C. G. Seligman). The latter interested Malinowski before Malinowski did his famous field work

[1] So far as the United States for the period before 1942 is concerned, detailed documentation for this and for statements that follow will be found in Clyde Kluckhohn, "The Influence of Psychiatry on Anthropology in America during the Past One Hundred Years." In: *One Hundred Years of American Psychiatry*. 1944. New York: Columbia University Press, pp. 589-617.

[2] Géza Róheim is not a valid exception because his fundamental outlook was that of a psychoanalyst rather than that of an anthropologist. There are, of course, a few genuine exceptions to this generalization. See, e.g., E. S. van Kloosterhuis, *Freud als Ethnoloog* (Amsterdam, 1933).

66

among the Trobriand Islanders, and the result was Malinowski's well-known attempt to refute the universality of the Oedipus Complex.

The publication of *Totem and Taboo* made cultural anthropologists aware—even if unfavorably aware—of psychoanalysis. Circumstances were not propitious. In France, Germany and the United States anthropology was at this time—to varying degree and for varying reasons—resolutely anti-psychological. Such psychological interest as remained active in anthropology at this time was found among the epigoni of the British evolutionary school. And these anthropologists were too intellectualistic to be prepared to understand or accept the depth approach of Freud. They were concerned only to "psychologize" in a half-hearted, mentalistic sort of way about ethnological data. In the second place, *Totem and Taboo* was calculated to irritate the most sensitive tissues of the anthropological body at this particular point. For anthropology was dominantly oriented to history as well as away from psychology. And *Totem and Taboo* struck anthropologists as outrageously speculative, psychologistic history. Moreover, Freud drew primarily upon authors (such as Sir James Frazer and Robertson-Smith) whose methods had been rejected by the anthropological profession before *Totem and Taboo* reached it. If Freud had only relied for his anthropology upon his age-mate, Franz Boas, the results of the first significant impact of psychoanalysis might have been altogether different!

Totem and Taboo may be—I am certain that in some respects it surely is—profound psychology. But as history it can hardly be taken seriously as other than metaphorical history. As Freud himself remarked in reply to the criticisms of the anthropologist, A. L. Kroeber, *Totem and*

Clyde K. Kluckhohn

Taboo is a "Just So" story. Boas—then the unchallenged pontiff of American anthropology—observed in 1920 that the origins of such phenomena as totemism are exceedingly complex and subject to influences from the total historical process that cannot be simply equated with the forces that control the psychology of the individual. Boas' criticisms were largely general and methodological, but those of Kroeber were exceedingly specific and detailed. He listed ten major factual and logical objections, most of which would require only minor editorial revisions after the lapse of 37 years. Other anthropological criticisms (e.g., those of Morris Opler and Margaret Mead) have been equally explicit and detailed. Freud himself in *Moses and Monotheism* took account of these objections at least to the extent of speaking of such things as the revolt of the tribal sons against the father not as a unique and specific historical event, but rather as "typical" and as "occurring again and again over thousands of years." It is therefore the more astonishing to read in Volume Two (p. 360) of Ernest Jones' great life of Freud:

I have, however, not come across any of their [anthropological] criticisms that contained serious arguments; mere expressions of disbelief seemed as adequate to them as similar expressions seemed to psychologists when Freud published his *Interpretation of Dreams.*

How did it happen that, in spite of these somewhat unfortunate beginnings, Freud has had his tremendous impact upon anthropology—at any rate in the United States during the last two decades? I believe there are two principal reasons—one mainly intellectual, the other more experiential and personal.

Because of developments that occurred largely within

American anthropology itself, anthropologists came more and more to feel the need for a usable psychology. We found—and this remains largely true to the present day— very little in academic psychology that seemed serviceable. But such psychoanalytic concepts as "ambivalence" did help us to understand hitherto puzzling phenomena of death beliefs and practices; "projection" certainly illuminated witchcraft anxieties; some similarities between compulsion neuroses and ritual activities were too unmistakable to be denied. One could give many more examples.

Moreover, there were the experiential factors that drew the psychoanalysts and the anthropologists together. Psychiatrists of all persuasions were showing that there was meaning in the most apparently chaotic and nonadaptive acts of the mentally ill. This struck an answering chord for the anthropologist, for he was engaged in demonstrating the fact that the seemingly bizarre patterns of non-Western cultures performed the same basic functions as did our familiar customs. The same amnesty that the psychoanalyst grants to incestuous dreams the anthropologist had learned to accede to strange customs. That is, both insisted that even "weird" behavior had significance in the economy of the individual or of the culture. There is also the circumstance that psychoanalysis developed and used a series of concepts (phantasy, libido, the unconscious, identification, projection) that applied specifically to human beings and which anthropologists found useful toward a better understanding of religion, art, and other symbolic phenomena. The main concepts of learning theory (drive, response, cue, and reinforcement), on the other hand, applied to animals at least as much as to humans. This is a great advantage for comparative psychology, but is too limited a repertoire for the phenomena with which anthropologists have to deal.

The dominant experience of cultural anthropologists had been as "unscientific"—in the narrow sense of that term—as that of psychoanalysts. Both groups operate with procedures that are essentially "clinical." Ordinarily the anthropologist working under field conditions has as little chance to do controlled experiments as has the psychoanalyst who sees his patient for an hour a day in the consulting room. The skilled of both professions do make predictions of a crude order and test them by subsequent observation. But these observations do not lend themselves to presentation in neat graphs nor to "t" tests. Indeed, both groups would maintain, without disparaging the indispensable importance of statistics for other purposes, that some of their main problems involve matters of form, position, and arrangement more than the incidence and clusterings of atomized variations. Probably in all culture, as well as in that aspect known as linguistics, the crucial issue is not that of size or frequency but of what point in what pattern. One may compare the principle of the circle, which does not depend upon measurement as such but upon a fixed patterning, even though measurements are necessary to draw any particular circle to specification. This particular pattern may be generalized in an equation, but the form of the circle can be recognized by those who are ignorant of the equation.

And so the anthropologist, however skeptical he may be of certain psychoanalytical dogmas, tends to feel in some measure at home in psychoanalytic psychology. He recognizes that there are certain similarities in the problems that confront him in describing and interpreting a culture and those met by a psychoanalyst in diagnosing a personality: the relationship between forms and meanings, between content and organization, between stability and change. It must also be freely recognized that psychoanalysis and much of cultural anthropology suffer from some similar defects and limitations.

Finally, let me try to sum up briefly and schematically what appear to me to have been the principal results of the impact of Freud upon anthropology thus far. First, psychoanalysis has enabled many anthropologists to gain a better understanding of and control over their principal instruments—themselves. A sizable number of American anthropologists have had didactic analyses. A fair number have even done control analyses. Second, cultural anthropologists, including those who have had no personal relationship to psychoanalysis beyond reading, now make as a routine matter certain observations and enquiries in field work that earlier were made but seldom or much less intensively. Boas (on non-psychoanalytic grounds) had emphasized the propriety of taking the individual as a subject of anthropological investigation. But detailed studies of the behavior of children, careful recording of dreams and free associations to them, the use of projective instruments—all these and other procedures came into anthropology directly or indirectly from psychoanalysis.

Third, there have been important collaborations in empirical and theoretical research. One may instance the Kardiner-Linton and Kardiner-DuBois undertakings. Fourth—and possibly in the long run the most significant of all—psychoanalysis has redirected the attention of anthropologists to the universals in culture and away from exclusive concentration upon cultural differences. Freud saw with beautiful clarity the consequences of such universals as the helplessness and dependency of infants, the influence of *both*[3] parents upon super-ego formation, the similarities in human anatomy and physiology the world over, and other inescapable "givens" of human life, regardless of culture. Situations making for the affection of one or both parents, for sibling rivalry, can to some extent be channeled this way or that by a culture, but they cannot be eliminated since the nuclear family is in one form or another a pan-human universal. A specific case of cultural universals upon which some of the British psychoanalysts (Fluegel, Money-Kyrle, Dicks) have written interestingly in late years is that of universal values or ethical norms.

Permit me to conclude with a slight paraphrase from Kroeber's "Totem and Taboo in Retrospect" (1939):

We anthropologists, though by no means completely converted to Freudian orthodoxy in every detail, nevertheless have met Freud, recognize the encounter as memorable, and herewith re-salute him.

---

[3] One might add that bi-parental reproduction of the super-ego is as useful in promoting adaptive variability as is bisexual biological reproduction.

72

FREUD'S INFLUENCE IN CONTEMPORARY CULTURE

Iago Galdston, M.D.

Executive Secretary, Committee on Medical Information
The New York Academy of Medicine

THERE IS an implied pretentiousness in the title of my paper which I am impelled to disavow. To treat amply of Freud's influence on contemporary culture one would need to possess both an encyclopedic intelligence—and, endless time. *You know* that I have not endless time, and *I* can asure you, that I do not have an encyclopedic intelligence. In 1936, when Freud's eightieth birthday was celebrated, Thomas Mann was called on to treat of a simpler theme namely Freud's influence on literature. Thomas Mann discharged his obligation in a singular and novel way. Thomas Mann spoke about Thomas Mann. He did this both deliberately and apologetically—saying to his audience—"Perhaps you will kindly permit me to continue for a while in this autobiographical strain, and not take it amiss if instead of speaking of Freud I speak of myself.[1]

For a while I thought of using the same dodge, but then realized I couldn't get away with it. For while Mann could

[1] Mann, T. *Freud, Goethe, Wagner.* New York, A. A. Knopf, 1937, p. 12.

be identified with, indeed impersonate, Literature, I could hardly impersonate Culture—with a capital C. I did, however, resolve my dilemma in the sensible resolution to talk *about* rather than *on* Freud and contemporary culture. That shrinks my commitments to the dimensions of my competences.

Initially I must define the sense in which I intend to treat of culture, and more precisely also the meaning of "influence." Culture is that field wherein the anthropologists, and after them the sociologists, have the greatest fun —waging, like the knights in Valhalla, their daily and unending semantic and ideological battles. I for one have no intention to enter their lists. Even though the restriction is arbitrary I intend to treat of culture as the embodiment of the hopes, faiths, beliefs, convictions, and aspirations which give distinction to the realms and ages of man. And I will not deal with culture in the abstract, but rather in particular, with those media wherein and whereby culture, so defined, is preserved and transmitted, and wherein its creativity is witnessed. You perceive that I am as wordy as the proverbial sociologist. What I intend to touch on is literature, the drama, some portion of the graphic arts, the vernaculars in general, and, to top it off, Existentialism. This, too, may seem pretentious, but let it not discourage you.

I must also define the meaning of "influence." It is not my intention to delineate Freud's direct influence on any given medium or on any creative artists. It is my plan, rather, to show how greatly Freud's theories, and his labors, were effective in the creation of a pervading climate of opinion, of an embracing atmosphere of comprehension and insight, so that none that "drew breath" could escape being affected, in one way or another.

But to judge of this we must orient ourselves to some starting point, and I would select for simplicity the medium of the novel, in the time of the Romantic period.

The Romantic period followed on that of the French Revolution. It embraces essentially the last decades of the eighteenth, and the first half of the nineteenth century. The novels of this period have certain distinctive features —but the term Romantic does not describe them. Indeed, they were not romantic in the original sense of that term —that is they were not fancied extravaganzas represented, say in the Chanson de Roland, in the Arthurian Tales, or in Ariosto's *Orlando Furioso*. These were tales rich in fancy, ingenious in plot, and counter-plot, and peopled with characters to which neither life nor experience affords a counterpart. They were magnificent creations—in the pure and uninhibited exercise of fancy. They were, in the pristine sense Romances, and so labeled. For the term romantic means: "extravagantly ideal, sentimental rather than rational; fanciful and visionary." The Romances, in a word, had no relation to life as it is experienced. Now the novels of the Romantic Period were not of this order. They embellished but they did not violate reality. Their heroes and heroines—Goethe's *Werther,* for example, and Schlegel's *Lucinde*—were not at all ethereal, but rather earth-earthy. Their experiences and adventures were such as do not commonly, yet might perchance, fall to the lot of the common man. Furthermore the writers of these novels were sustained by a faith in the transcending meaningfulness of life. That above everything else distinguishes the novel of the Romantic Period, and for that reason the period were better named—the Transcendentalist Period.

This transcendentalism was, in a measure, pantheistic. It glorified nature and the natural. In that respect it was anti-classical, for the classical was artificial rather than natural. Rousseau is counted among the initiators of Romanticism. His *La Nouvelle Héloïse,* his *Émile,* and his *Contrat Social* represented, as Ford Madox Ford describes them, "a general revolt against the stifling conventions of the classicism of the eighteenth century.[2] But the transcendentalism which animated the Romantic Period was more than a movement of protest, and vastly more than the roseate, Arcadian *Schwärmerei,* which it is commonly represented to have been. It had its dreams to dream, but also its lessons to teach. For if life is meaningful, then its meaning must, like a correct equation, tally in either direction: or, to paraphrase it in its Greek equivalent— Character and Destiny must be two components in reality which bear a reversible relationship.

It were too much, perhaps, to claim for Romantic Literature the fathomed grasp and the conscious exposition of this idea, yet it would not be, did we include in the ambient of literature not only the novel, but also poetry, the drama, and philosophy. Goethe's *Faust,* and particularly in its first part, is essentially an effulgent essay on Character and Destiny. But I feel more safe with the more modest claim. The Romantic Period, as mirrored in its novels, was naturalistic in the Rousseauist sense, that is, both realistic and romantic. Having withdrawn from the heroic and the palatial, the novelist could observe and treat of "life as is." This treatment of life is better witnessed in the Romantic writers of the non-Germanic countries: in the novels of Hawthorne and Herman Melville, in Lermontov's, *A Hero of Our Times,* and in the novels of Stendhal and Flaubert.

[2] Ford, F. M. *March of literature.* New York, Dial Press, 1938, p. 541.

It is among these authors that we first encounter the so-called psychological novel. Stendhal is credited with having initiated this order of novel with his *Le Rouge et le Noir* of 1831. But this, as most firsts, is simply the artifact of chronology. I mean, he did not originate the variety. Lermontov's epic appeared in 1836; Pushkin, counted a poet rather than a novelist, wrote *Eugeni Oneigin* in 1822-1829. Hawthorne's *Scarlet Letter* appeared in 1850 and Melville's *Moby Dick* in 1851. Each of these is pre-eminently a "psychological novel." Yet the point I want to make bears not on Stendhal's primacy. It is rather this: that as soon as the literary genius earnestly turns his competences to the perception, study, and description of man and his destinies, he must perforce psychologize.

In this connection it is of interest to note how many psychiatrists, notably psychoanalysts, have found among the authors of the Romantic Period writers whom they relish to dub pre-Freudian. Thus much has been made of Hawthorne's *Scarlet Letter* and Oliver Wendell Holmes' *Elsie Venner*. These are in effect significant psychological novels, but they were not written in a clairvoyant anticipation of Freud and of psychoanalysis. Rather they were written in the spirit and the intelligence of their time. And the time itself was intensely preoccupied with psychology. Indeed, and I anticipate Gregory Zilboorg will have treated this more fully, there was more of the pre-Freudian psychology in the psychology of the Romantic period than is to be found in its ample literature of novels and plays. Singly—Carus, Schubert, von Hartmann, names preeminent in the history of Romantic Medicine anticipated many of the elements that are to be found in Freud's metapsychology. Yet I must add, such anticipation does not make them pre-Freudians. Count these others, if you will, magnificent workers. Freud, however, was the sole architect and builder of his psychoanalysis.

Be that as it may, I need to get on with the talk, and the fact is that the Romantic Period which eventuated as a protest against the classicism of the eighteenth century, itself experienced both protest and revolt, and came to an end circa 1850. It came to an inglorious end, and thereafter to be called a Romantic was tantamount to having suffered the worst of insulting disparagements.

Romanticism gave way to Realism. Not transcendentalism nor the ultimate meaningfulness of life, but the singular problems of singular individuals, the orphan, the factory child, the prostitute, the thief, the murderer, became the subject of the representative novel. The better known exponents of this school of Realism, in the English language, were Dickens, Thackeray, and Samuel Butler; in French literature, Émile Zola is the outstanding example, and among the Germans, Hermann Sudermann and Gerhart Hauptmann. Both the Scandinavian and the Russian writers are eminently represented in this school—Björnson, Strindberg, and Knut Hamsun come to mind among the Scandinavians, and Turgenev, Dostoyevsky, Tolstoi, Chekhov, Andreyev, and Gorki among the Russians. This cluster of preeminent writers represents a broad spectrum of literary genius, and at first blush it may seem that they are too divergent, too singular, too distinctive in their respective creativity to be lumped under one category. In many respects, in literary style, for example, that is true indeed. And yet they do share in a common denominator. They treat of *problems* rather than of life transcendant. They are, if I be permitted to use the term, *typologists*. The problems they treat are those of social and economic adversity, of malignant heredity, of environmental stress, of political oppression, of personality defects. Their texts are not infrequently in the nature of social, economic, political, and cultural theses. In so far as they *are* psychologists they mirror the effects upon the individual of poverty, ignorance, heredity, disease, social hypocrisy and repression. The Russian writers perhaps treat more deeply of the socio-psychological reticulum that ensnares the individual. Though I doubt that Thomas Hardy, for example, would be found wanting, in comparison say to Gorki, or Dostoyevsky. But be that as it may, *this* fact is as true of Hardy as it is of Gorki and the rest, that the psychology of the Realist school was *deterministic.* The determinants are largely, if not entirely, *extraneous to the character,* and of a social, economic, environmental nature. The prostitute is such because she was betrayed, abandoned, poor, or otherwise corrupted. The thief is avenging himself on society. The murderer has been brought to despair and driven to violence. Not that these authors overlooked *character.* They have not! Neither Strindberg, nor Dostoyevsky, nor Gorki, had been so remiss. But *character* was deemed to be native. One was born with a given character, and the story invariably begins with that assumption.

In this respect the Realist writers were at one with the leading psychiatrists of their day—with Kraepelin, for example, and with Lombroso. Indeed they were in consonance with the emergent science of their age, which was in every respect, and in each department, belligerently deterministic. It was thus that the novel, and I might add, also the play, was *psychological in treatment, but not in insight.* Psychology mirrored experience, but did not illuminate it. There is a passage in Ford Madox Ford's *March of Literature* which I am moved to cite. It so well describes the deterministic psychology which animated the Realists. He is speaking of Dickens, Balzac, and Thackeray. "You always know beforehand," he wrote,[3] "what Dickens will do with the fraudulent lawyer on whose machinations hang the fate of a score of his characters; you always know beforehand how Balzac will deal with the million-franc financial crises with which his pages are scattered; and you always know beforehand the sort of best-club comment that Thackery in his own person will supply for every 20 pages or so of his characters' actions. There is no surprise." How could there be! Deterministic psychology, and determinism in general, *allows* for no surprises! It is thus that "given—a man has a cough, a hoarse voice, a black jowl and a wooden leg, not one of these novelists will let him take something to soften his voice, shave, or substitute a cork limb for the wooden peg that will stick out all over the story—ad nauseam." In brilliant contrast there is awakened in my memory the inspiring, the vivifying experience of Pirandello's *Six Characters in Search of an Author,* which I saw performed in my youth. There, as you may recall, the playwright who marshalled his characters, planning to manipulate them through his preconceived plot, finds himself taken over by the "characters." No less moving, as I recall it, was Sam Benelli's play, *The Jest,* in which both John and Lionel Barrymore shared the leading roles.

The dullness, the depressing aftermath of the Realist authors, both novelist and playwrights, are only now appreciable and comprehensible. They were not at the time when we were first exposed to them in our youth or, as I might phrase it, in our pre-Freudian days. For they did arouse sympathy and passion, and we were persuaded that

3 Ford, F. M. *loc cit.,* pp. 808-809.

we were the witnesses of "life in the raw." Besides, their hearts were on the "right side," not anatomically—but for "liberty" and against "reaction," for "justice" and "goodness" against "evil and corruption." Hugo and Ibsen; Strindberg and Zola; Tolstoi and Gorki! They still retain much of their magic, and no doubt *will* for many generations to come. But the rigging of their art is now perceptible as it was not in the days of our youth. And, would it be too much to say that Freud helped to clear our vision, and to sharpen our perception? I think not! He was not alone in this, but he became, for us, the embodiment of all the rest, the representative, the *Praesidium,* of that cultural emergence which cannot be named otherwise than Freudian.

It is not an easy task to define this cultural turn, even though the evidence of its effects is all about us. No small portion of the difficulty derives from the condition that it is so diffusely profaned. If a book or a play, a poem or a painting, treats of incest, homosexuality, a fetishism, or of a manifestly neurotic subject, it is more than likely to be labelled Freudian. Even those books distinguished for nothing but their superabundance of four-letter words are given this *affiche,* as if Freud invented pornography or opened the sluices of humanity's cloacal stream.

All this, however, is negative—it may clear the way for, but does not proffer, insight into the nature of the Freudian impact upon contemporary culture. The problem must be treated affirmatively: and that is perhaps best done through a series of affirmations stated categorically at first, and defended later. Thus—Freud challenged the prevailing philosophy of determinism. The emphasis here is on the term *prevailing.* For Freud too is a determinist, but his embrace of factors that "decide the issue," extends far beyond that deemed acceptable by his contemporaries. Take for example the "irrational" factor. The positivists, among the scientists, philosophers and authors, allowed for no surprises. But Freud demonstrated that life is full of surprises, that dreams, for example, are meaningful, that slips and errors and forgetting are meaningful. Freud did not deny the validity of rationality or of logical deductions. He did, however, demonstrate that logicality is only one attribute of being and experience, and that the paradox is more native to man than is the syllogism.

His was not a system or a philosophy of the irrational, as some would make it out to be. He rather underscored the fact that the rational *does* embrace the irrational,— that so-called error is meaningful and hence pregnant with rationality. He did all this not by simply playing with ideas born out of intuition as did the Romantics, but forged his conclusions in the travail of scientific research, study, testing and retesting.

Freud was no philosopher. He disclaimed all competence in philosophy and disavowed it. It is rather *we* who interpret *him* philosophically. Freud did not perceive, as we *can,* his position in the stream of cultural eventuation. Freud charted the trans-uterine emergence of character. He plotted the shores and shoals, the Scylla and Charybdis, that man must pass ere he reaches the haven of effective maturity, and *the ultimate* in self-fulfilment. Character, in the Greek sense, Freud demonstrated, is only partly given, the rest is attained in the adventures of living. There is a fatality that hangs over man, but, Freud proved, it is not implacable.

Freud was a psychiatrist, far more than he was a philosopher. Freud brought into our awareness the primal impulsions of life. In addition to the categories of time, place,

and the immediacies of reality, there is a fourth category—
that of life emergent. And it is the greater of the four, and
oft prevails even *against* the rest. The Romantics knew all
this, and so did the ancient Greeks before them. But the
Greeks knew it deductively, and the Romantics intuitively.
Freud, however, not merely affirmed all this, but demonstrated it. He helped make the blind to see and the lame
to walk. And as a result, derivative rather than direct,
since his day all of our thinking and feeling, and representation of life, has been changed. These operations have
acquired a new dimension: the dimension, not only of
extension but also of depth. That Freudian psychology is
called Depth Psychology is very proper indeed.

I must try to make my meaning more clear. Freud came
upon a world that was naively sober and earnest. Truth,
it held, was truth, and fact—fact. Relationships were patent, or were to be made so. There was, in other words, no
hindside, to truth, or fact, or relations. There they stood,
stark naked and bold, for all that chose to see. Reality was
reality, and neither ever was nor ever could be anything
else. Reality for example could never be the symbolic,
conventional, representation of another reality standing
behind it, which itself was but a symbol for something
else, and so on ad infinitum. Everything was so very patent
to the Victorians. Had not Herbert Spencer accounted for
everything but the Unknowable? Nor was it otherwise in
art, music, the drama, philosophy, philology, and so on.
Not that everything was already known, but rather that
the ways to knowledge had been amply mastered.

Into this all-too-cock-certain world Freud threw the
bombshell of symbolism. Reality, he asserted, stood not
monolithically by itself, but in a series of relatednesses, and
was in effect but the latest symbolic representation of that

relatedness. Dreams spoke in symbols, but so also do we, waking, for words have meaning and representations, far above and behind their explicit conveyance. So has art, and the drama. Things are not really *always* what they seem. They may be *that,* but commonly are *more beside.* Is it any wonder then that the Victorian world recoiled in horror? But fortunately not all of it. There were a few that also had heard the Siren song. They were not followers of Freud, at least not in the beginning. They rather shared with him in this deeper vision of being and reality. The Impressionist painters come to mind; Verlaine and Baudelaire, the poets, and Schnitzler, the dramatist and novelist. There were others too—Nietzsche, for example, but I cannot catalogue them all. The cardinal point to be noted is that Freud, so to say, *structuralized* his deeper vision of being and reality, organized it and communicated it so that others might share in it. This, may I add, Freud accomplished not in his system of therapeutics, that is in his psychoanalysis, but rather in his system of Metapsychology. Because he so effectively structuralized his understanding of being and reality, it is preeminently proper to speak of *Freud's* influence on contemporary culture.

These influences are readily perceived in literature, that is in the novel, drama, in poetry, in literary criticism, in biography, and in autobiography. They are to be witnessed no less clearly but in different respects in the graphic arts, and in what I term the vernaculars.

Freud's metapsychology (what I have called his deep vision of being and reality) deals with the full spectrum of life, with well-being no less than with illness, with the normal as well as with the abnormal. But Freud was initially a therapist, one who treated the sick. He drew insight from his experiences with the sick. He was a psychopathologist *before* he became a psychophysiologist. Literature, for all-to-obvious reasons, seized upon Freudian psychopathology, and made it its own domain. This is, of course, in the best traditions of Aristotelian poetics. But as a result—Freudian psychopathology is better known to the public than is his metapsychology. Since there is so much pathology within and about us, this may not be at all bad. Indeed it must profit us to recognize and to understand psychopathology—as and when we encounter it. And to this end literature has made and is making its notable contributions. It is my impression that the playwrights are preeminent in this field—possibly because plays are generally compounded of action—while in the novel the author can dally on the scenery and soliloquize. But the contemporary novels and plays alike reflect the influence of Freud. They are not merely psychological as are those of Stendhal, that is psychologically descriptive—they are rather analytical and dynamic. They illuminate the operations of psychic forces within and upon the experiences and ultimate destinies of man—among men.

I have mentioned Schnitzler, the friend and contemporary of Freud. Two of his works are, to my mind, superb illustrations of what I have in mind. One is the play *Reigen,* the other his novel *Frau Beate und ihr Sohn.* The first is a kaleidoscopic *ronde* of erotic communion—between a number of pairs, each one of whom has shared the partner of another coupling. This superb work contains a minimum of prurience and of salaciousness, but it does profoundly portray how Eros is conditioned in the settings of varying interpersonal relations. *Frau Beate und ihr Sohn* deals with the motif of unconscious incest, but in such wise as to transfix one's soul with the humility of deep wonderment.

The other playwright that comes to my mind, as it must also to yours, is our own Eugene O'Neil, and among his many and truly great plays the one that I feel best bears on our theme is his *Emperor Jones*.

It is not possible to cite other illustrative and supportive authors and playwrights. Beside there has been published a good book, badly named *Freud on Broadway,* which deals with this subject broadly and competently. I'll merely call this book in witness and stop there.

Of literary criticism, biography, and autobiography, there is no need to say much. You will recall, I am sure, the rash of debunking biographies which first appeared in the 'twenties, and which remained "in style" for a decade or more. These were, so to say, only weakly Freudian. They were rather reactive to the "stuffed shirt" patterns of the earlier biographers. But how deeply the writing of biography—in this instance autobiography—has been affected by Freud, one can perceive in that composed by Stanley Hall, who brought Freud to the United States in 1909, and in the other, written lately by my good friend Norbert Wiener.

I am aware that I have treated these items somewhat gingerly, but that is because I want to devote what little time is left me to the subject of *the vernaculars. Vernacular* is the term applied to a regional language. But it has a second meaning, of which the one I cited is derivative. It also means non-classical. The advent of the vulgar tongues, e.g., French, Italian, Spanish,—vulgar because they are not Latin or Greek—unbridled the intellectual and artistic potentialities of man. For all their glories, the classic tongues in time hobbled man's spirit, hedged in his creativity, and constrained his inventiveness. Since then every new vernacular, every new communication medium, has contributed to the greater growth and the more ample enrichment of the human mind and spirit. But while originally the vernaculars were only vulgar tongues, that is language in the pristine sense, they have since grown in variety. Thus there are new vernaculars in mathematics, in logic, in painting, in poetry, indeed in all the modalities of communication. You need but think of the motion picture, television, and most significantly of the animated cartoon, to perceive at once both the meaning and the enormous creativity of the new vernacular. And to these developments—by indirection—Freud contributed greatly and profoundly. Was it not Freud who challenged the naive objectivity and the plain rationalism of the nineteenth century? Did he not above all others reveal to us the function of the symbol? Well then, if the word stands but for the symbol, why not expound and expand the symbol in the word, and thereby come closer to indwelling meaning. The poet always endeavored to attain to indwelling meaning, hence his poetic license. His license is broader now since the time of Freud: witness in T. S. Eliot, E. E. Cummings, and Gertrude Stein. Schnitzler in *Fräulein Else,* and Joyce in *Ulysses* employed a new vernacular, that of the stream of consciousness. Patently this is related to, if not a direct derivative of, the Freudian "free association." O'Neil in several of his plays made his characters to speak out, and to experience, their repressed and unconscious thoughts and feelings. This, too, is in the nature of "a new vernacular." But it is in the graphic arts that we witness most clearly the enfranchising, emancipating influences of Freud's emphasis on the symbolizing articulatedness of the psyche. The "humble contraption," the *mobile,* is in effect the limpid, animated, embodiment of the artists' hoary doctrines of masses, proportions, and relations. It is a multi-dimensional, shimmering exposition of the theory and philosophy of art that lies entombed in scores of musty volumes. The "mobile" is Freudian in spirit and speaks in eloquent witness of his impact on both painting and sculpture. The pointillist painters, the Impressionists, the painters and sculptors of abstractions, and the Surrealists, are and have been creating new vernaculars, and thereby enriching the human psyche, and enlarging the dimensions of our cultural life. It matters little whether what they produce is Art—by your or my definition. Bethink ye rather that even Shakespeare babbled in his infancy. Nor should you misread the meaning of my words. I know that the Impressionists predate Freud, even as did Schnitzler's *Anatol*. I am certain that neither Chagall nor Dali drew their inspiration from Freud. And I am persuaded that Freud, who surrounded himself with Egyptian, Etruscan, and Roman antiquities, was not partial to modernity in Art. But all this is really beside the point. Freud was not merely Freud, he was the embodiment, the realization, the exponential force of a transcending movement, "whose waves came awash upon the many shores." The impact of Freud upon culture is akin to that of Darwin upon Science—no discipline remains unaffected by the concept of evolution.

And now comes my final salvo! I am persuaded that the philosophy of Existentialism shares the Freudian vision of being and experience. Existentialism is a loosely used *label*. It is affixed, to my mind, in gross error, to a good deal of degenerate and morbid literature. It is perverted by a coterie of craven and defeated souls, into a philosophy of swineish hedonism, and desperate permissiveness. It is not any of this that I refer to as Existentialism. I have in mind rather the works of Kierkegaard, of Heidegger, of

Jaspers, and of Husserl. I mean that most illuminating treatment of the problem of "meaning and experience," of "purpose and achievement," the answer proffered by Existentialism to the vulgar query—"Of what good is life anyway."

In Existentialism I perceive this answer, that "goodness apart from the experience'" is a sham concept and a false query. The warrant for being lies in being, the meaning of existence is realized and achieved in existing. Freud too expounded this philosophy in his Metapsychology. It is embraced in his juxtaposition of Eros and Thanatos—in what he termed the life instinct and the death instinct.

Here I come to the end of my exposition *about* The Influence of Freud on Contemporary Culture, and a discomfiting suspicion dawns upon me. In that last analysis I fear me that quite like Thomas Mann, but more unwittingly, I have talked less about my subject and more about myself—that is, about my nodding acquaintance with Culture.

INDEX

(references to tables are given by page and (t); references to foot-notes are given by page and (f)).

Index

Ego functions
  effect on by infantile experience, 32
  in development and regression, 36
  in learning, 36
Eliot, T. S., 87
Elsie Venner, 77
emergence of character, 82
Émile, 76
emotional auras of ideas, 50
dynamics, 10(t)
emotionally disturbed, 22
emotions, correlatable with bodily functions, 40
Emperor Jones, 86
energy, biological, 8(t)
ergasias, the, 9(t)
Eros, in setting of interpersonal relations, 85
Eros-libido, 8(t)
Eros-Thanatos, 8(t), 44, 89
error meaningful, 82
etiological factors from past experience, 32
etiology
  formulation of specific, 35
  psychological and social, 20
existentialism, 44, 88, 89
existentialists, 16
experience, past
  etiological factors from, 32
  importance in functioning of individual, 12
experiences
  childhood and family, 12, 13(t)
  infantile, effect on ego functions, 32
  life, 37
  stressful, 49

family, nuclear, 37, 77
fatality, not implacable, 82
Faust, 76
Ferenczi, Sandor, 5(t), 15(t)
fixation, 32
Flechsig clinic, 56
Flaubert, Gustav, 76

Fliess, Wilhelm, 36(f)
Flint, Austin, 56
Fluegel, J. C., 72
Ford, Ford Madox, 76, 76(f), 79, 80, 80(f)
"four doctors of Baltimore," 56
France, Anatole, 17
Franco-Prussian war, 54
Frau Beate und ihr Sohn, 85
Fräulein Else, 87
Frazer, Sir James, 67
free association, 87
Freud
  analysis of sexuality, 7(t)
  background of genius, 16, 17
  capacity for integration shown, 7(t), 8(t)
  concepts of impulses and behavior, 9, 10
  contributions compared to those of scientists, 10-11
  conviction of destiny, 17
  cultural eventuation, position in, 82
  development of human personality, scheme of, 22
  determinism challenged, 81, 82
  diplegia, cerebral, 16
  dissidence, non-acceptance of, 19
  doctor-patient relationship, 33
  embodiment of cultural emergence, 81
  experimental method opposed, 39
  exponential force of transcending movement, 88
  family relationships, 16
  group dynamics, root in, 50
  history of medicine, place in, 59
  impact on anthropology, 66-72
  impact on contemporary culture, 73-89
  importance of individuality, 19
  importance of past experience, 12
  in the clinic, 16
  in the perspective in medical history, 53-65
  indivisibility of human personality, 64

93

Index

Index